Andy Porter works as a counsellor/group worker in mental health and as a non-violent direct action trainer for CND. He is a founder member of the Brighton SERA (Socialist Environment and Resources Association) group and has campaigned on social and environmental issues in the anti-nuclear movement.

Martin Spence is a video researcher/production worker and a founder member of the Anti-Nuclear Campaign. He has recently campaigned with Newcastle Trades Council, Tyneside Anti-Nuclear Campaign and CND. He is a member of the Labour Party.

Roy Thompson works for the East Anglian Alliance Against Nuclear Power, campaigning principally against Sizewell 'B'. He was involved in founding the Jobs from Warmth group in Ipswich, and is active in the Labour Party.

The Energy Fix

Towards a Socialist Energy Strategy

Andy Porter, Martin Spence, Roy Thompson

Pluto  Press

London   Sydney   Dover New Hampshire

First published in 1986 by Pluto Press Limited,
The Works, 105a Torriano Avenue, London NW5 2RX
and Pluto Press Australia Limited, PO Box 199, Leichhardt,
New South Wales 2040, Australia. Also Pluto Press,
51 Washington Street, Dover, New Hampshire 03820 USA

7   6   5   4   3   2   1

90   89   88   87   86

Typeset by Rapidset and Design Ltd, London WC1
Printed in Great Britain by Guernsey Press Co. Limited,
Guernsey, C.I.

British Library Cataloguing in Publication Data
Porter, Andy
  The energy fix: towards a socialist energy
  strategy.
  1. Energy policy—Great Britain
  I. Title   II. Spence, Martin
  III. Thompson, Roy
  333.79′0941   HD9502.G72
  ISBN 0 7453 0070 7

Contents

Acknowledgements

The authors gratefully acknowledge the helpful comments and criticisms given by the following people during the writing of this book: Huw Beynon, Gary Craig, Dave Elliot, John Irvine, Nick Jagger, Richard Kuper, Garry Jenkins, Ian Miles, Nigel Mortimer and Ken Ternent. We would like also to thank Pat Cadwallender for help with the research for chapter 6, Dominy Hamilton, who did some of the early typing and Dave Lowson for the index. All errors and omissions are, of course, entirely the responsibility of the authors.

We would particularly like to thank Myrtle Nixon and Barbara Lambert for the regular houseroom freely given for meetings during the four-year gestation of this work. It was never going to be easy writing a book with the authors living in three far-flung parts of the country. Without the use of Myrtle's front room it would have been impossible.

List of abbreviations

AGR	advanced gas-cooled reactor
ANC	Anti-Nuclear Campaign
BGC	British Gas Corporation
BNFL	British Nuclear Fuels Ltd
BNOC	British National Oil Corporation
BWR	boiling water reactor
CAITS	Centre for Alternative Industrial and Technological Systems
CEGB	Central Electricity Generating Board
CHP	combined heat and power
DH	district heating
ERR	Earth Resources Research
FPIC	Fuel and Powers Industries Committee
GDP	gross domestic product
GE	General Electric
GEC	General Electric Co. Ltd
GW	gigawatt
IIED	International Institute for Environment and Development
KW	kilowatt
LWR	light water reactor
mtce	million tons of coal equivalent
MW	megawatt
NATTA	Network for Alternative Technology and Technology Assessment
NCAT	National Centre for Alternative Technology
NCB	National Coal Board
NEI	Northern Engineering Industries
NIC	newly industrializing country

NNC	National Nuclear Corporation
NUM	National Union of Mineworkers
OPEC	Organization of Petroleum Exporting Countries
PJ	petajoule
PWR	pressurized water reactor
RTZ	Rio Tinto Zinc Ltd
SERA	Socialist Environment and Resources Association
SGHWR	steam-generating heavy water reactor
SSEB	South of Scotland Electricity Board
THORP	thermal oxide reprocessing plant
UKAEA	United Kingdom Atomic Energy Authority

A Note on Energy Categories and Units

To take into account the losses incurred when energy is converted from its primary form (e.g. coal) to its fuel end-use (e.g.
lighting a house), energy is split into three separate categories:
primary energy, delivered energy and end-use energy. Primary
energy is the energy content of the initial fuel. Delivered energy
is the energy delivered to the customer (i.e. the primary energy
less the energy lost in its transformation and transportation).
End-use energy is the proportion of the delivered energy put to
good use (the rest being lost due to inefficiencies in its application).

The introduction of these categories obviously means that care
must be taken when comparing forecasts, etc., ensuring that, for
example, primary energy from one forecast is not compared with
delivered energy from another. The introduction of renewable
energy sources can confuse the issue since the idea of primary
energy doesn't really suit these technologies. For instance, considering electricity generation by coal or by wind: the efficiency
of a power station is around 30 per cent, i.e. 30 per cent of the
primary energy is converted to electricity, but for a wind
generator the primary energy source, the wind, is not something
that must be closely accounted for – it is a renewable source.
Therefore, when considering the use of renewable energy
sources in terms of primary energy, care must be taken to say
whether the renewable source is saving a certain amount of conventional primary fuel or making an actual contribution.

The field of energy units, too, can be confusing. Where possible throughout this book we have tried to refer always to million

tonnes of coal equivalent (mtce) – the energy equivalent to the energy content of 1 million tonnes of coal, which, while imprecise due to different coals having different energy contents, is a popular and widely used unit.

Other units we have used in some tables are joules – the international standard (SI) unit for energy, where 1 mtce = 25.7 petajoules. Also, reference is made to gigawatts (GW) and megawatts (MW), the standard units of electric power.

Introduction

Every winter in Britain, around 800,000 elderly people are at risk from hypothermia.[1] In the period 1975-80, 3,837 people 'officially' died as a result of the condition.[2]

Since it was opened the nuclear waste reprocessing plant at Windscale has discharged 250 kilograms of plutonium into the Irish Sea – enough to give 250 million lethal doses of lung cancer.[3]

In the years 1950-84, 738 coal pits in the UK were closed, often causing hardship and suffering in the communities dependent on them for survival.[4]

The list of horrors that are inflicted upon society in the name of energy policy is a long one and it grows every year. Energy, and its supply, is a fundamental prerequisite of any society. Without it we could not eat, we could not house ourselves and we could not travel from one point to another. We need energy to keep ourselves warm in winter, to provide light at night, and to supply power for our homes and industry.

Yet, as a subject, it is rarely discussed by those on the left (other than as a specific issue such as the 1984-5 miners' dispute), and when discussed by others, such as the Green movement, it tends to be in utopian terms of what could be achieved 'if only' society were shaped in a different fashion.

Britain has a wealth of energy resources and the opportunity to develop energy provision in new directions that are safe, comparatively cheap and do far less damage to the environment. But these resources are not being used wisely and the new options are not being taken up. Why is this? The starting point to the answer is to realize that energy policy is neither neutral nor merely technical: it reflects specific class interests. Under capitalism, policy is structured to serve those interests, rather than to meet human needs or to take into account damage done to the environment.

This book puts forward an explicitly socialist approach to energy as a crucial focus for any strategy aimed at improving society. There is a pressing need for a debate on energy policy which recognizes its role in underwriting a whole range of other social and economic policies. The provision of energy resources, or the lack of such provision, can predetermine or pre-empt options in other fields. As a simple example: any conventional attempt at reindustrialization in the UK would take for granted the need for growing energy inputs, especially in the form of electricity. For all recent British governments this would in turn imply building new power stations, probably nuclear, at vast public expense. Apart from the crucial environmental and safety issues, such expenditure would also pre-empt investment resources and thus hinder the development of other areas such as education, health or welfare. Britain would thus be faced with an apparently inescapable choice between industrial growth *or* welfare spending.

By contrast, reindustrialization which is linked to a policy of energy conservation and energy efficiency could create more jobs, bring more benefits to a wider section of the community, *and* avoid the false choice between industrial growth or social welfare.

Throughout this book there will be frequent references to 'socialism' and 'capitalism'. It is necessary to explain what we mean by these words.

We follow Marx in seeing capitalism as a system in which goods and services are produced or provided *not* directly to meet individual or social needs, but for the profit that their production or provision will realize. We follow Marx in seeing the direction of capitalist development hinging around the struggle between two distinct economic classes: those who own or control the means of production; and the vast majority who don't, and can only live by selling their ability to work. The long-term interests of these two classes are opposed: capital's drive for profitability leads to a chaotic unplanned growth on the one hand, and to periodic attempts to reduce workers' living standards on the other.

This simple explanation is far from adequate, of course. In Britain, as in all other Western states, we also have to take into account intermediate strata, state expenditure, nationalized industries and state-funded welfare. These are important parts of the picture – the state sector allows some areas of production that do not directly yield profit, and welfare allows some workers to survive without working – but they do not alter the fundamental nature of the system itself.

One fundamental aspect is that capital must continually expand in pursuit of profit, and this expansion is always essentially *unplanned*. In modern capitalism, and especially in sectors such as energy, planning appears to be far more extensive than in Marx's day: it operates now on the level of national governments and international monopolies, rather than merely within small independent factories or businesses. This extension of planning does not mean, however, that the system as a whole is any more under control than it was in the nineteenth century. Then, as now, planning by one body takes place in the context of competition with another. Then, as now, capital must expand in order to survive, and without economic growth one firm's expansion is necessarily another's collapse.

This constant dynamism faces capitalism with constant crises because it can never stabilize; because no one fraction of capital is ever safe from destruction through competition, because whilst hooked on growth, it can never consistently meet the material and social needs of its workforce; *and* because its technology has developed to the extent that production decisions by individual corporations now have global impact on human populations and ecological systems far beyond the ability of those corporations to predict or control.

Energy provision in the UK, like other economic sectors, reflects this overall pattern of unplanned capitalist growth. The future depends on those of us who must live by selling our labour, on our success in visualizing a more rational and humane alternative to the present chaos, and on our effectiveness in translating this vision into action for social change.

Wherever capitalism has existed, the socialist vision has existed within it – as an inspiration behind workers' resistance, as a programme for change, or as a future utopia. Socialist practice and ideals have taken many forms over the years, but there is nevertheless a common vision of a post-capitalist society in which production is democratically planned on the basis of human need. And for a sector as fundamental as energy, the need to remove it from domination by market forces is all the more pressing.

Part 1 of the book provides an essential background to understanding the politics of energy, placing British options firmly in a global context. After an analysis of world energy trends, the impact of the world market on two specific energy sectors in Britain is examined. The range of energy choices facing Britain in the years ahead is then discussed.

Part 2 examines various political approaches to energy policy in Britain in recent years. Following a critical analysis of the records of the Labour Party and trade union movement, and of the Tory governments since 1979, a number of 'alternative energy' forecasts are examined, together with associated ideas of the Green movement.

In the third and final part of the book the emphasis is on the future. After setting out a framework for a socialist theory of the politics of energy, the range of working-class initiatives which are building towards a socialist practice are discussed. Finally, proposals for an integrated energy strategy for the late 1980s and 1990s, as part of a wider socialist economic programme, are set out.

PART 1

1. World energy trends

Energy and the crisis

In any discussion on the politics of energy, 1973 is an obvious date on which to focus. It was the year of the first OPEC 'oil shock', and in Britain it was the year of a miners' strike and the 'three-day week' which led to the fall of the Tory government in early 1974. Many conventional explanations of the economic crisis, which has blighted the Western economies since the early 1970s, point to the 1973 OPEC oil price rise as a major cause. Closer examination reveals, however, that the 'oil shock' was a symptom, rather than a cause, of the crisis.

By the late 1960s the 'long boom' of the postwar period was burning itself out. The rate of profit in the basic industries around which the boom had been structured – primarily steel and engineering – was stubbornly low. The Vietnam war had also taken its toll on the US economy, and this inevitably fed through to the world capitalist economy as a whole, given the USA's central position within it. A mini-boom in 1971-2 could not disguise the long-term trend towards some sort of crash. The single factor of higher oil prices undoubtedly contributed to the crisis, but can hardly be said to have caused it.

Similarly, OPEC is often blamed for the international financial instability which developed from the early 1970s. On the one hand, oil prices put enormous sums of money into the hands of oil-exporting countries; and on the other, an international lending spree took off from the early 1970s, with large loans from Western banks to newly industrializing Third World countries and to Eastern Europe. But it is rather spurious to argue that one thing caused the other, when international lending was running at about four times the rate of OPEC deposits into the world banking system. Clearly the Western banks were playing their own game, and were using a lot of money other than OPEC oil revenues.

The sustained economic crisis of the 1970s and 1980s was not therefore caused by the 'oil shocks' or by an 'energy crisis'. The energy industries, including oil which is the most powerful of them, must be understood as part of the wider economic system. They are certainly a vital part, but are not in any sense independent from the system as a whole. To explain the economic crisis as a result of the 'oil shock' is a convenient way of avoiding the real issue – the inherent limitations and contradictions of the capitalist system itself.

Energy trends in the advanced capitalist countries

In North America, Western Europe and Japan, the most important single energy trend from the late 1940s to the early 1970s was the sustained and deliberate creation of oil dependency – and in Western Europe and Japan this meant dependence on imported oil (see Chapter 2). By 1973 Western Europe was dependent on oil for 60 per cent of its energy needs[1] while Japan's reliance was even higher at 77 per cent.[2] In the USA oil provided 47 per cent of energy requirements in 1973.[3]

Dependency on this scale could not be wished away overnight. In Western Europe, and even more so in Japan, measures were taken after 1973 to reduce overall energy consumption and especially to reduce oil consumption. By the early 1980s Japanese oil consumption was down to about 50 per cent of total consumption,[4] and in Western Europe to about 49 per cent;[5] but quite clearly oil was still a major contributor to energy supply. In the USA, which was traditionally less dependent on imported oil, the trend actually went the other way: whilst oil consumption went from 47 per cent to 49 per cent, oil imports rose between 1973 and 1978 from 27 per cent to 47 per cent,[6] and only declined slightly thereafter.[7] The continuing appetite of the USA economy for vast quantities of oil has undoubtedly contributed to the continuing global importance of the oil companies and oil-exporting countries.

In the early 1980s, the international oil market has been weak, faced with a problem of overproduction and falling prices. OPEC faces rivalry and even war between its member states, and is also confronted by the emergence of three new oil provinces: in the North Sea, Mexico and the North Slope in Alaska. This might seem to indicate that 'oil shocks' are now well behind us, but such a judgement would be premature.

In 1978 too, the international oil market seemed to have settled down – only to be thrown into confusion again by the Iranian Revolution. The second 'oil shock' of 1978-9 was not the result of any great reliance of the international market upon Iranian oil – in fact Iranian production represented only a fraction of world production and Saudi Arabia has always been a far more significant OPEC producer. The threefold price rise of 1978-9 was inevitable in a world which continued to rely heavily on oil exports from the Gulf, but which was no longer able to impose an acceptable degree of 'stability' in the Gulf region. The stability of the pre-OPEC era was essentially a reflection of the overbearing power of the USA in that period. In the more volatile conditions of the 1980s, sustained stability in the world oil market is no longer possible.

Despite the continuing importance of oil in the advanced capitalist countries, other energy sources are becoming more important. One result of the 'oil shocks' was that governments in the capitalist countries did look to energy alternatives. Perhaps the most spectacular, and certainly the most controversial, of these was nuclear power. The early 1970s were boom years for the world nuclear industry, with an average of 34 new reactors ordered per annum in the capitalist world from 1971 to 1975.[8] The 'oil shock' was a boost to this development in general propaganda terms, allowing nuclear power to pose as the 'answer' to the 'energy crisis'. But it would be quite wrong to suggest that the nuclear boom came as a direct result of the 'oil shock'. Its roots go back well into the 1960s, when sizeable national nuclear industries were built up in most advanced capitalist countries for strategic, economic and military reasons. By the early 1970s, these industries were looking for orders to keep their productive capacity employed, with the result that this period saw not only a mushrooming of domestic programmes (especially in the USA, France, West Germany and Canada), but also the start of an export drive into the newly industrializing countries (NICs) of the Third World (specifically Argentina, Brazil, South Korea and Taiwan).

However, the boom in the nuclear industry was short-lived. Over-optimistic technical assumptions, rising costs and a growing political and environmental opposition to nuclear power, started to take their toll from the mid-1970s. This happened first in the USA, where cancellations and deferrals outnumbered new reactor orders from 1974 onwards. There have been some cutbacks too in West Germany and France, while the UK programme has always been characterized by delay and indecision. It would certainly be premature to claim that the nuclear industry is finished: the corporations involved are some of the biggest in the world – strategic, high-technology engineering concerns, enjoying links with their domestic states. However, the industry is still in difficulty, with International Atomic Energy Authority projections of future nuclear capacity cut by another 28 per cent in 1984.[9] Firms are desperately pushing to expand export markets in the Third World. Current developments in the British nuclear programme can only be understood when put into this global context, as will be seen in Chapter 2.

Alongside the drive to nuclear power, the 1970s saw renewed development of fossil fuels as direct or indirect substitutes for oil. In Western Europe coal had been run down in the 1950s and 1960s, as part of the strategy of turning to cheap oil (see Chapter 2). It was now revived in some countries, and especially in the UK, where the 1974 'Plan for Coal' envisaged a return to levels of production not seen since the early 1950s. But by the mid-1980s the EEC Commission was again advocating a rundown of Western European coal. However, coal's renaissance continues at a global level.

World coal reserves are enormous, but very unevenly distributed. 85 to 95 per cent are concentrated in just three countries: the USA, USSR and China.[10] In the newly developing international coal market, which grew by 30 per cent between 1978 and 1981,[11] the USA is a dominant element, producing and consuming more than half the capitalist world's coal. US private capital has moved into coal on a major scale, with the oil companies taking a dominant role as part of their strategy of diversifying into different energy sectors: in 1980, 7 of the USA's 15 largest coal producers were oil companies.[12] The other main coal-exporting countries at present are Australia, South Africa, Colombia and Poland, but their recoverable reserves are only a fraction of those of the USSR and China. If these two non-capitalist giants moved into the export of coal they could quickly come to rival the USA and would give the world market a highly political character which would be further complicated by the fact that the main coal importers are the capitalist countries of Western Europe.

The other fossil fuel to see major development in the 1970s is natural gas. As with coal, reserves are very unevenly distributed: the USSR holds 40 per cent of proven world reserves and the next largest holder is Iran, with 15 per cent.[13] The USA is also well-endowed and its use of natural gas rose even during the cheap oil era of 1950 to 1973. In Western Europe, natural gas development and consumption has increased spectacularly during the 1970s, spurred on by higher oil prices. It rose from 12 per cent of Western European energy consumption in 1973 to 17 per cent in 1980.[14] In the UK its expansion was even more spectacular with gas sales tripling between 1970 and 1980.[15]

Finally, there is the whole area of energy conservation and efficiency. The record here varies very much from one capitalist country to another. The USA, despite a history of profligate energy consumption and consequently enormous scope for energy saving, has made little headway, and in fact *increased* its energy consumption between 1973 and 1979.[16] In Western Europe energy efficiency increased, but only in terms of 'taking up the slack'.[17] In Japan, where the pressures were most intense, but the scope for improvement most limited, significant energy savings have been made.[18]

These differing achievements raise an important point about energy conservation and indeed about wider changes in energy use. Serious conservation and efficiency requires not merely a patching-up exercise to stop current wastage, but *investment* in energy-efficient systems, technologies and buildings. Energy conservation requires the allocation of capital resources. If this decision is left to the market, the resources are only likely to be made available if there is overall growth and market confidence; but by the same token, conditions of overall growth imply that fuel prices are generally regarded as 'acceptable', thus obviating the motive for investment in energy conservation. It is clear that serious attention to energy conservation means stepping beyond the dubious logic of price signals and short-term profitability. It is also highly significant that the advanced capitalist country that has made most progress in this area, Japan, is also the country where co-ordinated planning is most evident in the economy; and the country which has made the least progress, the USA, is the closest to a 'free market' economy.

The overall picture in the advanced capitalist countries is therefore of increasing internationalization and increasing unpredictability in energy markets. Oil continues to occupy central stage, but international trade in coal, gas and nuclear power is fast developing. Different countries are likely to dominate these different markets. For oil, the OPEC countries remain important but non-OPEC producers can also have a significant impact; coal is dominated by the USA, Colombia, Australia and South Africa; nuclear power by the USA, France and West Germany. However, it should never be forgotten that in all these areas future world markets may be strongly influenced by the actions of the non-capitalist countries.

Of the world's 4 billion people, 1.5 billion live in countries which are developing on a non-capitalist basis. These societies – in the USSR, East Europe and elsewhere in Asia, Africa and Latin America – are highly significant in any consideration of world energy trends, and their actions will have a profound impact upon the advanced capitalist countries and upon the Third World. This is especially true of the USSR, the world's first and largest country to industrialize on a non-capitalist basis.

Energy trends in the USSR

From the First Five Year Plan in the late 1920s through to the 1950s, the Soviet economy was based on coal and hydroelectric power. However, oil and gas development was given high priority from the late 1950s, and nuclear power was greatly expanded from 1970. By 1975 the USSR was the world's leading oil producer, and by 1980 its pattern of energy consumption had shifted to the point where 70 per cent of its needs came from oil or gas.[19]

Soviet oil is supplied to its economic partners in Eastern Europe and elsewhere, but sustained efforts have been made to sell it in Western Europe as well, since the 1960s. With the 1973 'oil shock' its attractiveness to Western European customers increased, and the same was true for Soviet natural gas exports. By 1981 oil and gas sales accounted for 75 per cent of the USSR's exports to the West,[20] making them a crucial source of hard currency earnings. However, this growing orientation of Soviet energy exports towards the West has been achieved at the expense of its partners in Eastern Europe. Prices charged to them have been raised, following OPEC's lead, and a series of bitter arguments have resulted.

The crucial point is that even the USSR, with an unparalleled wealth of natural resources, is being pulled, apparently not unwillingly, into the world energy market. This is largely because energy exports provide it with the means of tackling domestic economic problems. Soviet agriculture is chronically inefficient, while industry is plagued by a deep-rooted technological conservatism. Hard currency earnings from oil and gas sales allow the USSR to offset these problems through imports of grain and Western technology. Much has been written on the possibility of Western Europe becoming 'over-dependent' on Soviet energy supplies, and vulnerable to political blackmail. However, the other side of the coin is that the USSR is also dependent on earnings from its energy exports. Paradoxically, therefore, it has a vested interest in renewed capitalist growth and prosperity in order to maintain the level of sales.

This integration of the USSR into world energy markets is also seen in other sectors besides oil and gas. For many years the USSR exercised a tight regime in its international nuclear dealings. It has provided nuclear reactors to other non-capitalist countries in Eastern Europe and elsewhere, but has retained absolute control over the preparation, supply and reprocessing of fuel. More recently, faced with a determined nuclear export drive from Western Europe and the USA, it has started to cultivate its own export market outside the circle of its regular economic partners. It has sought reactor sales in Turkey, Libya, Syria and Bangladesh and has provided potentially military nuclear material to Argentina.

Coal is a further area in which the USSR is turning to the world market. Its recoverable coal reserves are second only to those of the USA[21] but the bulk of the new coal reserves is overwhelmingly in the east, in East Siberia, far from the main industrial and urban centres of the European USSR. Just as West Siberian gasfields were exploited for export to Western Europe, so the East Siberian coalfields may be developed with Japan intended as a major export market. Japanese capital is indeed playing a role in the development of these resources.

In all these energy sectors, Soviet policy is increasingly interlinked with developments in the capitalist world. There is a further major energy source which has always been given a high priority in the USSR, and which can generate energy exports: hydro power. As far back as the First Five Year Plan the Dnieper Dam was a key industrial project, and enormous hydroelectric power stations are still being built, especially on the giant rivers of East Siberia. Four of the five largest hydroelectric power stations in the world are in the USSR and via the Soviet United Power Grid their electricity is transmitted westwards for export to Eastern Europe. Clearly a potential also exists for further electricity sales to Western Europe, or perhaps to China.

Soviet involvement in world energy markets is therefore an ambiguous development for all parties concerned. For the USSR there is a clear danger that its energy planning will come to be dominated by export considerations and by market conditions in the capitalist world. While not necessarily threatening a restoration of capitalism, this could lead to severe domestic tensions. But on the other hand, to abandon energy exports and to tackle internal economic problems without the benefit of Western grain and technology, will *also* lead to serious tensions. From the point of view of the capitalist countries, meanwhile, the sheer size of Soviet energy resources holds out the possibility of the USSR exercising an 'unacceptable' influence in the markets for natural gas and, potentially, for coal.

Diverse trends in the Third World

The very term 'Third World' was always a glib generalization and is becoming increasingly dubious as a useful label. It covers a wide range of countries, from the wealthy oil-exporting Gulf states, to the export-oriented NICs, to the poverty-stricken lands of the Sahel and elsewhere. However, it does carry a residual value, in that it indicates one common and essential characteristic of these countries: all of them are forced to operate in a world market dominated by and structured around the interests of the advanced capitalist countries. Even the most 'successful' of the NICs, such as South Korea, are experiencing an unbalanced and essentially dependent form of economic development, dictated by the world market and financed by massive foreign loans. In any country the energy infrastructure is both a prerequisite for, and a determinant of, wider economic development. Third World energy policies therefore represent a focal point for Third World economic problems in general and it is important to look at these issues in some detail.

Economic development in the world today means industrialization, and industrialization demands adequate energy inputs. Because oil is so flexible and mobile, and because of the established structure of oil dependency elsewhere in the world, Third World industrialization necessarily requires access to oil[22], primarily for transport. Oil must be paid for, however, which means that economic development depends on a pre-existing degree of credit-worthiness in the eyes of the West's financial institutions. There is no doubt that the cost of oil imports has contributed to the spectacular debts accumulated by some NICs, such as Argentina, Brazil and South Korea. However, as has already been mentioned, oil price rises cannot be the *sole* explanation for the debt explosion, especially when it is remembered that Mexico, a net oil exporter, is also one of the Third World's biggest debtors. The crucial point is that industrialization, oil imports and credit-worthiness are all interlinked, meaning that countries which are regarded as bad risks never even get off the ground.

Oil itself is not enough, however. Modern industrial development demands that energy also be available as electricity (see Chapter 6). Electricity output in the Third World is growing much faster than in the advanced capitalist countries, and two-thirds of it is used in industry.[23] It can be generated by burning oil, gas or coal, or from hydro-power, nuclear power or renewable sources. Renewables may seem the logical choice, especially solar power in tropical regions, but where rapid economic development is prioritized there is great pressure to fall back onto existing and tried technologies. Consequently, expertise and technology tend to be imported from advanced industrial countries in order to reproduce those countries' large capital-intensive power stations and transmission grids. After all, where fossil fuel resources are scarce or unexplored, and renewables undeveloped, it may seem logical to turn to technologies already pioneered by the advanced industrial countries, including nuclear power.

The nuclear export drive discussed above initially concentrated on the NICs, but has now broadened so that the list of Third World countries with nuclear facilities, or nuclear ambitions, is growing fast: Argentina, Brazil, Mexico, Iran, Iraq, India, Pakistan, South Korea, Taiwan and the Philippines all have nuclear programmes. So too do South Africa and Israel, which fit with difficulty into the 'Third World' category. Other countries have plans to develop nuclear power: Chile, Algeria, Libya, Morocco, Egypt, Syria, Turkey, Bangladesh, Indonesia and Thailand.

A nuclear power programme is necessarily complex, costly and specialized. It involves not merely building power stations, but also access to nuclear fuel and, ideally, possession of enrichment and fuel fabrication facilities, and to waste storage or reprocessing plants. Even in the advanced capitalist countries, nuclear programmes have faltered due to the technical and financial burdens they impose (see Chapter 2). These problems are even more acute in the Third World, and it is clearly impossible for poor Third World countries to launch self-sufficient, domestically financed nuclear programmes. Third World governments with nuclear ambitions are generally forced to turn to advanced industrial countries both for finance and for nuclear technology and this has generally meant the advanced capitalist countries, though the USSR is also now supplying some Third World countries. Whoever the supplier, nuclear imports can only lead to further dependency, both technological and financial. Perhaps the classic illustration of this is to be seen in the Philippines, where a nuclear power station has been built at great expense. It was constructed by a US corporation, financed by US loans, and if it becomes fully operational it will supply electricity to a US military base and to an 'enterprise zone' dominated by US multi-nationals.[24] Clearly this has little to do with the autonomous development of the Philippines economy.

The fact that Third World nuclear programmes continue to be developed, despite these evident drawbacks, indicates that something else is at stake in addition to economic development: the bomb. The nature of nuclear technology is such that any avowedly 'peaceful' nuclear programme can be used as a smoke screen for the development of nuclear weapons, and there is little doubt that the acquisition of such weapons is a primary aim for many Third World governments. Countries with proven or suspected nuclear weapons capability include Argentina, Brazil, Iraq, India, Pakistan, South Africa, Israel and Libya.

Nuclear power is not the only energy source to swallow up scarce technical and financial resources, however. Even such a potentially valuable local source as hydro-power can be exploited in an entirely inappropriate and destructive way. Hydro-power should be a significant contributor to Third World economic development. South America, Africa and parts of Asia are relatively poorly endowed with fossil fuels, but have a tremendous untouched hydro-power potential. Whereas Europe and the USA have harnessed 75 per cent of their hydro capacity, Africa has so far exploited only 4 per cent.[25] There are however major problems with hydroelectric power schemes as presently conceived and implemented. First, they are frequently developed as prestige projects, requiring foreign technology and finance and generating electricity beyond the capacity of the local grid. In Nepal, for example, the World Bank has financed an enormous, export-oriented hydroelectric power scheme which will take 27 years to complete, whereas a series of small hydro projects could have been generating useful local power within five years.[26] Second, the priority given to gross power output is frequently allowed to override considerations of environmental damage done by the dams. The massive flooding associated with large hydroelectric schemes leads to the dislocation of whole communities, unbalancing of the local ecosystem, and the loss of good agricultural land.

This leads to the link between energy and food – an essential link in the Third World context, because in many ways energy needs and food are competing for the same resources. The chemical inputs into modern agriculture, which make it so productive in terms of gross yield, are derived from the same hydrocarbons which provide most of the world's energy – oil, gas and coal. In energy terms, modern agriculture is actually very inefficient: it typically consumes five times more energy than it produces, in contrast to the so-called 'primitive' techniques, such as 'slash-and-burn', which consume only one-twentieth or one-fiftieth of their energy output.[27] However, 'primitive' techniques are incapable of the intensive, concentrated, gross output of modern agriculture. Partly for this reason, and also because of the export-oriented cash-crop basis of their own agriculture, in the early 1980s Third World countries were importing 100 million tonnes of grain per annum from the capital- and energy-intensive agribusiness of the capitalist world.[28]

Modern agricultural techniques have been introduced unevenly in the Third World, with the use of fertilisers and other chemical inputs being concentrated on 'high yield varieties' of crop. By the same token these resources are channelled to the biggest, and therefore more 'efficient' farmers, thus consolidating rural class differentiations. Stress has also been laid on cash crops for export, rather than food crops for domestic consumption. The result is that growing millions of rural poor are effectively pushed out of the market and off the best land. They can only respond by trying to intensify their traditional agricultural practices, but without knowledge of soil conservation techniques or chemical additives to supplement the soil's own resources, this leads to soil exhaustion and erosion. The UN has estimated that between 5 million and 7 million hectares of arable land are lost each year through soil erosion, much of it in the Third World.[29]

This process is linked to a chronic fuel crisis which affects the same marginalized millions in Asia, Africa and Latin America. For these people, effectively excluded from the market, the major fuel for cooking and heating is firewood gathered from the surrounding countryside. Eighty per cent of the Third World's wood use is as fuel, mostly on a non-commercial basis.[30] Consequently, acute wood shortages now exist in large areas of the Third World as forests and shrubs are destroyed, leading to deforestation and contributing to further soil erosion. Furthermore, when firewood runs out, the most easily available substitutes are crop residues and cow dung, which would otherwise be used as much-needed fertilizer. The UN has estimated that the cow dung burned each year would represent a potential grain output equivalent to 20 per cent of the Third World's grain imports.[31]

Oil-importing Third World countries are therefore caught in a complex vicious circle of underdevelopment, encompassing industry and agriculture, in which energy policy is a crucial component. Economic development, both industrial and agricultural, demands access to fossil fuels and their chemical by-products and above all it demands access to oil. These resources are needed not only to provide power for transport and industry, but also to stave off the cumulative environmental disaster in the countryside and to draw the productive energies of the marginalized population into the national market and the national economy. Basic economic development in the Third World must therefore involve rising energy consumption. Renewable energy resources could make a major contribution to meeting these needs, as could exploration work aimed at locating further fossil fuel reserves which undoubtedly exist throughout the Third World. The problem is that Western corporations often monopolize the necessary resources and expertise, but are generally not interested in exploring these options; and the very urgency of the problem, together with less honourable motives such as military or political ambitions, push many Third World governments into a suffocating dependency on foreign finance, technology and fuel supplies. The problem thus reproduces itself and the vicious circle is closed.

Conclusions

The 'energy crisis' which hit the capitalist world in the early 1970s is not a crisis of absolute physical shortage of energy resources. The oil is *not* going to run out in the foreseeable future. The 'energy crisis' was, and is, a reflection of the deeper and broader crisis of the capitalist system and of the shifting balance of power in the world. It reflects developments not only in the West, but also in the non-capitalist countries, and in the Third World.

Broadly, the trend is towards world energy markets which are increasingly integrated and increasingly volatile. Oil has already shown itself to be a potent means of political leverage. The emerging global markets in coal and natural gas will be no less 'political' and the spread of nuclear technology has obvious military and political implications. No country can be isolated from these broad trends. The question is, will they merely reinforce existing inequalities, or can they be used to open up new options for socialism and democracy?

2. British energy policy and the world market

Energy trends in the world at large vary from one country to another, depending on local economic, political and natural conditions. At a global level a picture is already emerging of increasing integration but also of instability in world energy markets. Here, the emphasis is upon Britain and British energy policy, looking at the ways in which global energy trends have helped to mould policy in this country in the past 40 years. The focus is upon two specific sectors: oil and (at rather greater length) nuclear power.

Oil

US oil companies have long exercised a heavy influence on the world market, but not an unchallenged influence. From the early twentieth century the development of the world oil industry was dominated by a long-running rivalry between the USA and Britain. Each had its own large oil companies, each had its own geographical sphere of influence, and each realized the strategic value of the commodity and was prepared to deploy diplomatic and even military means to protect its companies' interests. Thus the Anglo-Persian Oil Co. (now BP) was set up before the First World War on government initiative, with a specific brief of safeguarding British oil interests in Iran.

The Second World War may have seen the USA and UK ostensibly fighting as allies, but their oil rivalry was neither suspended nor forgotten. US companies used the war to achieve a new dominance in Saudi Arabia at Britain's expense, but the UK retained its strongholds in Kuwait and Iran, and these were significant assets: in 1950 Iran accounted for 20 per cent of Middle

Eastern production.[1] The USA's chance in Iran came in 1951, when Mossadeq's radical nationalist government hit at Britain by nationalizing the oil industry. For a while the USA flirted with Mossadeq, whose own orientation was definitely anti-British rather than anti-American,[2] but by 1953 the USA agreed he was too disruptive an influence and a joint Anglo-American operation was launched which overthrew the government and installed the young Shah. The price of US co-operation, however, was that BP lost its 100 per cent holding in Iranian oil. The booty was shared out with US and other companies and BP had to settle for 40 per cent.[3]

The Iranian operation marked the USA's victory in the long-running oil rivalry with Britain, but Britain has remained a major force in the world industry nevertheless, through BP and through the British holding in Shell. This marks the UK out from the other advanced capitalist countries in Western Europe, and from Japan, which have been much less significant in oil production or in the possession of oil reserves.

However, the UK's relatively influential position did not prevent its being profoundly affected, like the rest of Western Europe, by US policy from the late 1940s. In 1947, the USA launched its Marshall Plan to finance European economic recovery. Marshall Aid was a policy of enlightened self-interest on the part of the USA. It was intended to help Europe back to prosperity, to avoid a new depression and to keep it in the US orbit.[4] At the same time, however, it structured European recovery so as to create long-term markets for US companies and attractive prospects for future US investment.

The structure of European energy supply was a crucial component in this strategy. In the late 1940s and early 1950s, much of Western Europe's energy needs were met by indigenous coal production and many European miners' unions had a strong communist presence.[5] In the name of free enterprise, capitalism and anti-communism, the Marshall Plan created conditions for the replacement of politically vulnerable Western European coal by imported oil. Of the $13 billion aid given under the Plan, $2 billion was specifically to finance oil imports.[6]

In Western Europe, as a result of these external pressures, the pattern of energy consumption shifted radically with oil replacing coal as the staple fuel. Production in the main coal-producing countries fell by 1974 to 43 per cent of its 1948 level.[7] In the UK itself, production declined from 210 million tonnes in the early 1950s, to 115 million tonnes in 1975.[8] Furthermore, this absolute decline in coal output occurred in the context of rising overall energy demand, so that the *proportion* of British energy needs met by coal plummeted from 90 per cent in the late 1940s to 35 per cent in the early 1970s.[9] Meanwhile, oil consumption expanded from 10 per cent of primary energy in 1950 to 48 per cent in 1972.[10]

While the UK and the rest of Western Europe were drifting into oil dependency, things were moving on elsewhere. The bulk of West European oil supplies no longer came from North America, which in 1950 still accounted for half of world output. By 1970 the new cheap Middle Eastern oilfields were by far the largest single element in a vastly expanded market.[11]

However, exploitation of oil resources in the Middle East had other consequences as well. The rapid development of capitalist production, and capitalist social relations, was a profound shock to these essentially feudal societies. In some cases entirely new ruling classes emerged. In others, such as Saudi Arabia, traditional rulers reoriented themselves to the new situation. The general tendency, however, was a much greater awareness on the part of ruling groups in oil-exporting countries of the economic and political realities of the modern world economy, and of their own key role within it. The first hint of this development was the formation of the Organization of Petroleum Exporting Countries (OPEC) in 1960. Its confirmation came with the assertiveness of Gaddafi's new regime in Libya in 1969, and its culmination was the oil embargo and price rise of 1973. The result of the embargo was a significant shift in the balance of power within the world oil market, away from the private oil companies and towards the oil-exporting states; and also a significant shift within the capitalist world, in favour of the USA and to the detriment of Western Europe and Japan.

The implications of these shifts need to be spelled out. It is certainly not the case that oil companies have suffered in terms of reduced profits: on the contrary, their profits hit record levels following the OPEC price rises of 1973-4 and 1978-9.[12] However, this rise in company profits was dwarfed by the much greater and more significant rise in the revenues of the oil-producing countries.[13] Even in the early 1980s, with a relatively weak oil market and considerable downward pressure on prices, this essential shift in the balance of power was not reversed. Private oil companies obviously exert influence on the market, but the single most important element in determining world production and price levels is still OPEC.

The oil price rise of 1973-4 also signalled changing relationships between the advanced capitalist countries. Oil dependency in Western Europe and Japan, as explained above, was encouraged by the USA as a matter of foreign and commercial policy. However, the very success of this strategy subsequently presented the USA with new problems, as Western Europe and Japan not only recovered but started to compete successfully with US companies on the world market. In this context, the OPEC oil embargo was an opportunity for the USA to hit back at its newly emergent capitalist rivals.

Compared to Western Europe and Japan, the USA was a comparatively minor oil importer in the early 1970s. The sharp rise in the price of oil therefore hit Western Europe and Japan disproportionately hard and conferred a new relative advantage on the US economy, while also boosting the profits of US-based oil companies. The OPEC oil embargo could therefore be seen as the result of a tactical, de facto alliance between the oil exporting states, the US state and the (largely) US-based oil companies, against the oil-importing countries of Western Europe and Japan.

Britain, in 1973, as an oil-importing Western European country, shared in the general problem and reacted in the obvious way by cutting oil consumption. Petroleum consumption fell from 48 per cent of primary energy in 1972 to 36 per cent in 1982,[14] while in the EEC countries as a whole oil fell from 61 per cent of total energy consumption in 1973 to 49 per cent in 1982.[15]

However, Britain was in rather a special position. Unlike the other large industrial capitalist countries of Western Europe it has extensive oil reserves: reserves which, in 1973, were known to exist but had not yet begun to be commercially exploited. The fact that these reserves are mainly offshore, in the North Sea, means that production is much more difficult, dangerous and expensive than is onshore production in an area like the Middle East. Consequently, North Sea oil production only 'makes sense', in commercial terms, in the context of generally high world oil prices. In other words, it only makes sense *because* of the OPEC price rises of 1973-4 and 1978-9,[16] and because of the continuing role of OPEC in maintaining a relatively high price. North Sea oil is a post-OPEC phenomenon, relying for its viability on the maintenance of a politically imposed price structure on the world oil market.

It is also post-OPEC in terms of the balance of power between the oil companies and the state. North Sea production is, of course, carried out by private oil companies, but within a legal and fiscal framework laid down by the British state, and with the constant prompting and guidance of that state. It is the government which controls the issue of licences, decides on the allocation of areas for exploration and production, lays down the tax regime, and strongly influences the marketing arrangements. To the end of 1984, nine rounds of licences in the North Sea were issued and successive governments have become increasingly sophisticated in using licences to direct the nature and pace of North Sea oil development.

This is not to imply that different governments have pursued identical policies. On the contrary, there is a considerable difference between the approach of the 1974-9 Labour government – with its emphasis on a widening public stake in the North Sea through the British National Oil Corporation (BNOC) – and the Tories, who have privatized the state's oil assets and abolished BNOC (see Chapters 4 and 5). However, the most significant difference has been an accident of timing rather than a matter of deliberate policy. In 1979, when Thatcher took office from Callaghan, North Sea output was still relatively low. It was the Tory government which was to inherit the North Sea windfall.

The Tories' approach has been to treat North Sea oil, not as an energy resource to be valued for its contribution to useful production and social welfare, but as an energy *commodity*, regarded as a source of financial subsidy to the national economy and a convenient medium for underwriting the Tories' overall economic strategy (see Chapter 5). The keynotes to this policy are therefore a major role for private capital and sustained governmental effort to maintain rapid and high levels of oil production. The irony is that North Sea oil is thus being used to subsidize an economic policy based on the principles of free enterprise and market forces; but the North Sea oil industry relies for its very existence upon state intervention, upon a relatively high price and therefore upon the continued domination of the world oil market by the oil-exporting states of OPEC.

These ironies and contradictions have come out in various ways. Both Thatcher and Lawson have publicly stated that they oppose any 'artificial' interference with the price of oil,[17] but at the same time their own oil minister has engaged in correspondence with the oil companies, seeking an agreement whereby the price of oil would be kept up.[18] On the other hand, over a period of many weeks in late 1984-early 1985, when the world price of oil looked as if it would slide badly, and with OPEC trying to prevent this, the British government simply did nothing; it refused to name a price for its oil. Despite being a major producer and actor on the world market, the UK behaved as if it was merely observing that market. This attitude was seen again in early 1985 when the government announced that it was going to abolish BNOC altogether, having already reduced it to a shadow of its former self. The avowed reason for abolition was that world oil trading was now dominated by short-term deals and the spot market, so that BNOC had outlived its usefulness. However, even at this point the Tories felt it necessary to keep residual powers over the physical movement of oil through a pipeline regulation agency. This is the constant, inescapable contradiction of Tory oil policy: the government is caught between its practical need to play an interventionist role in order to influence North Sea production and if possible to maintain price levels, and its ideological need not to be *seen* to be intervening.

Two major conclusions flow from this brief survey of British oil policy. Firstly, policy has, through the postwar period, been dictated by oil's status as an internationally traded energy *commodity*, rather than its character as an invaluable energy *resource*. The exploitation of this commodity in the 1950s and 1960s was deeply influenced by the foreign policy objectives of the US state and the commercial objectives of US capital. More recently, North Sea oil has been used directly to subsidize the economic and social policies of the Tory Party.

Secondly, the mechanics of this exploitation have changed, as economic and political development has shifted the balance of power within the world oil market away from private capital and towards the oil-exporting states, including the UK itself. This situation has been exploited by the Tories, though it faces them with major contradictions in terms of their own professed ideology.

Finally, it needs to be said that the changing balance of power in the world oil industry could open up other, quite different, possibilities. The state's effective domination of North Sea oil development *could* be used in different political conditions as a lever for implementing a radical, long-term depletion policy as part of a planned energy strategy for Britain. This option is *still* open.

Nuclear power

The origins of the British nuclear power programme, both civil and military, lie in the Manhattan Project: the collaborative Allied effort, during the Second World War, to develop an atomic bomb. Both Britain and Canada fed into the project, but it was funded and controlled by the USA and once the war was over the USA put an end to the collaboration.

These beginnings, in a major military project developed for reasons of state, have left their stamp on the nuclear industry. Unlike oil, nuclear power does not have its roots in the dynamics of private capitalist growth: it is born of strategic considerations, both military and economic, on the part of governments. These state decisions have not been made in a vacuum. The British nuclear power programme has often been analysed in terms of technical arguments and official debates, within the institutions of the state,[19] but these analyses fail to capture the essential global context which has structured and guided state policy. In Britain's case, the development of nuclear technology is best understood in terms of a 40-year contest with the dominant nuclear power, the USA.

The decision to develop a British bomb, taken by the 1945 Labour government, can in part be explained by a continuing 'great power' mentality within the government and the state apparatus,[20] plus a sense of pique at the new, unco-operative attitude of the USA.[21] Despite these apparently superficial motivations, the decision itself, once taken, was of major importance. Furthermore, it established the theme which has dominated British nuclear developments ever since: the tension between subservience to the USA on one hand and a stubborn desire for technological independence on the other.

The reactor programmes

Nuclear power emerged from the nuclear weapons programme as a spin-off. It was partly motivated, no doubt, by moral misgivings on the part of scientists who had worked on the bomb and who now wished to apply their knowledge for the benefit of society. The new intellectual challenge of nuclear power was a further incentive.[22] Economic considerations also played their part: if already existing military nuclear facilities could be made to yield non-military services as well, then at the very least this would be a useful subsidy to the military programme.

From the mid-1950s the UK launched an independent, major and initially very successful nuclear power programme, based on the 'Magnox' reactors originally designed as military plutonium factories. Early hopes of private investment were soon dashed, and it was decided that all developments should be kept within government agencies.[23] This led to the formation of the United Kingdom Atomic Energy Authority (UKAEA) in 1954, with powers to carry out research and development into atomic energy with a large degree of independence. In 1955 an ambitious programme of 2,000 megawatts was announced, and in 1956 the Queen opened the world's first commercial nuclear power station at Calder Hall in Cumbria in a blaze of publicity. Calder

Hall was, in fact, a converted plutonium factory.[24] The size of the nuclear power programme was increased again at the time of the Suez Crisis. Throughout this period, Britain was regarded as the world leader in nuclear power development and it was widely expected that nuclear power could provide large-scale and cheap energy for the future. Problems of safety, and radioactive pollution, were yet to make their public appearance.

However, the UK's nuclear success was seen as a challenge by the USA which was itself seeking to dominate nuclear power development in Western Europe. Its strategy on nuclear power was essentially similar to its encouragement of oil dependency (see p.20). The intention was to promote European economic recovery; open up markets for US investment and exports; create long-term dependency on the USA for technology, fuel, services and expertise; and contribute to the coherence of the US-dominated Western Alliance against a perceived Soviet threat.[25] In 1958-9 the USA concluded a treaty with Euratom, the newly formed European nuclear association, offering US government assistance for any countries prepared to buy US-designed light water reactors (LWRs). Since the USA had a virtual monopoly in the supply of enriched uranium fuel this was a difficult offer for the European countries to refuse. The turning point for the USA came in 1958 when Italy, despite having previously bought a British Magnox reactor, chose an American light water reactor in exchange for long-term capital loans to cover the cost of construction. The UK was unable to match the USA's marketing strategy and further LWR orders soon followed in France, Belgium and West Germany.[26]

This US nuclear export drive was based on the emergence of a large domestic market and the growing confidence of US private capital not only to build reactors, but also, through privately owned power utilities, to order them. A symbolic breakthrough came in 1963 when the New Jersey Central Power and Light Co. ordered a 500 megawatt reactor without the added incentive of federal assistance. The multinational reactor suppliers now came into their own. Both Westinghouse and General Electric (GE, not to be confused with Britain's GEC) had embarked on nuclear careers as government contractors, working on various aspects of

the nuclear weapons and nuclear-powered submarine programmes. Throughout the 1950s they had US government contracts to
build up technical expertise in nuclear power generation and had
been supported in their export plans by US government financial
backing, channelled through the Export-Import Bank. By the
early 1960s they were ready to start creating a genuine international nuclear market with their rival LWR designs: Westinghouse with its pressurized water reactor (PWR), and GE with its
boiling water reactor (BWR).[27]

In Britain, the role of private capital was rather less dynamic.
The government tried in the 1950s to sponsor five consortia of
power-engineering and civil-engineering firms in order to inject a
measure of 'healthy competition' into the industry, but by 1960
two of the five had collapsed. By default, if not by design, the
state therefore continued to play a crucial role in dictating the
overall direction of nuclear developments. In the face of the successful US strategy, which had wiped out Britain's early lead and
cornered the lucrative Western European market, there were
strong pressures to concentrate on developing a new British reactor to challenge the US LWRs.

In 1964 a new nuclear programme of 5,000 megawatts was
announced, and the Central Electricity Generating Board
(CEGB) received tenders from the three remaining consortia.
Two of them offered to build American LWRs: English Electric
suggested Westinghouse's PWR, and the Nuclear Power Group
offered GE's BWR. These two groups were in effect proposing
that Britain should abandon its attempt at technological independence, accept the realities of the world market and follow the
other European countries in basing its nuclear programme on US
reactor types. However, they hedged their bets by also offering
to build advanced gas-cooled reactors (AGRs), the new, exclusively British design which had emerged from the Magnox fam-
ily. The third consortium, Atomic Power Constructions, offered
only an AGR.

Government influence ensured that the Atomic Power Construction bid was accepted. The economic rationale for this decision was dubious as the BWR was cheaper,[28] and the technological rationale was also flawed, as became clear in the following

years. The only existing AGR was a small prototype and serious problems emerged in 'scaling up'. As one technical problem followed another, the delays in the first AGR at Dungeness in Kent mounted up and costs escalated. The fiasco was compounded at a commercial level when Atomic Power Constructions collapsed in 1969.

Further AGR contracts continued to be placed with other companies but they fared little better. Hinkley Point and Hunterston were finished in 1976, six years late and 33 per cent above cost estimates. Hartlepool started up nine years late, cost five times more than originally estimated and had to be shut down again eight days after starting up. Heysham arrived some seven years behind schedule. The AGR programme threw the credibility of the British nuclear industry into serious doubt.

By the early 1970s it had become clear that drastic measures were needed. In the late 1960s, a series of takeovers and mergers had been sponsored by the Labour government, aimed at rationalizing and streamlining British industry. As part of this process GEC emerged as the major force in UK engineering, and acquired English Electric along with its licence to build the Westinghouse PWR in Britain. GEC was therefore well placed when the Tory government reorganized the nuclear industry in 1973, centralizing all reactor construction activities in a single body, the National Nuclear Corporation (NNC). The NNC was effectively built around GEC. GEC had the largest single private stake in the Corporation (30 per cent), was given managerial control, and supplied the first NNC Chairman in Lord Aldington who was also a GEC Vice-Chairman.[29]

The formation of the NNC and the new influence of GEC renewed the pressure for the American PWR to be adopted as the British standard reactor. Within the CEGB and the civil service, the commitment to the PWR had now become significant, powerful enough to dictate policy proposals on electricity supply as a whole. For instance, in 1972, before the establishment of the NNC, the CEGB Chairman, Sir Arthur Hawkins, had testified to a House of Commons Committee that the Board envisaged ordering only three or four new power stations, of which one would be nuclear. By the following year, testifying again to the same Committee, but in circumstances more propitious to the PWR, he proposed that no less than 32 new power stations were needed, all of them to be PWRs.[30]

The incoming Labour government in 1974 was strongly wedded to the promotion of British technology, but the costly fiasco of the AGR programme led it temporarily to favour a new British option, the steam-generating heavy water reactor (SGHWR). A campaign of studied non-co-operation by the CEGB and GEC ensured that the SGHWR never got off the ground and by 1976 it was dead.

The PWR lobby was meanwhile building up its institutional support, aided by a new pro-nuclear mood in the establishment as a result of the 1973-4 oil price rise and the simultaneous miners' strike which led to the fall of the Tories. The PWR was now being backed not only by GEC and the CEGB but also by senior civil servants in the Department of Energy and the Central Policy Review Staff (this latter unit having been described by Tony Benn as 'the lynchpin of the civil service network'[31]. Industrialists in other companies such as Rolls Royce (which builds small PWRs for nuclear-powered submarines) added their weight to the cause.

However, this widening support for a particular reactor design cannot be explained in terms of personalities. The global context was crucial in creating conditions for this scientific-industrial lobby. In the early 1970s, the world nuclear industry saw an unprecedented boom: from 1971 to 1975, 169 reactor orders were placed with the nuclear corporations of the advanced capitalist countries.[32] By 1974, however, the bubble was already fit to burst in the biggest single market, the USA. Cost escalation, technical problems and growing public opposition meant that from 1974 cancellations or deferrals outnumbered new orders.[33] This collapse of the US domestic market came on top of a longer-term process whereby the balance of new reactor orders was shifting anyway, away from the US corporations and towards new companies in Western Europe and Japan.[34] *All* the advanced capitalist countries were under pressure in the 1970s, as the boom subsided, and in the West as a whole the nuclear industry was operating at only 46 per cent capacity.[35] But the US corporations, who had dominated the world market for years and had seen their domestic market collapse most dramatically, were under the greatest strain. In this context it was only natural that the US nuclear corporations should seek to keep their capacity employed, and realize a return on investments already made, through an energetic export drive. Similarly, it was only natural that Westinghouse, which had been seeking to break into the British market for years via its successive licensees English Electric and GEC, should renew these efforts.

The resulting pressures were manifested in the Department of Energy when Benn, who headed the Department from 1976 to 1979, found his civil servants effectively implementing their own, pro-PWR nuclear policy.[36] All Benn's efforts were required to hold the PWR lobby temporarily at bay and to opt instead for two more AGRs at Torness and Heysham.

May 1979 saw the coming of the Thatcher government and the creation of far more favourable conditions for the PWR (see p. 84). The Tories' priority was not only to develop nuclear power as a strategic alternative to coal, but also to find a reactor which could demonstrably be built to cost, to time and as part of a series of reactors. In December 1979, therefore, the new government announced its intention to build ten nuclear power stations, the first of them to be a Westinghouse PWR of about 1,200 megawatt capacity. After 20 years, the US PWR seemed finally to have broken into the British market.

However, the PWR was not quite home and dry. First, it has had to cope with the 25-month saga of the Sizewell Inquiry, which has represented a major delay whatever its final decision. Second, it has to face continuing opposition from within the British nuclear industry from those private companies and institutional lobbies whose best interests lie with a continued AGR programme. Within the industry, opposition is symbolized by Northern Engineering Industries (NEI) and the other companies in the NNC with which it is closely associated, such as Whessoe and McAlpines. NEI invested in a major refit of its NEI-Nuclear Systems subsidiary on the expectation of continued AGR work: in 1984 the whole facility was virtually mothballed and 1,200 workers made redundant.[37] Babcock International at

Renfrew similarly made large investments in new plant and machinery which may be rendered useless by a PWR programme.[38] Other authoritative voices in or close to the nuclear industry, such as the South of Scotland Electricity Board and Lord Kearton, have argued strongly for a continued AGR programme, and senior figures within the UKAEA also privately favour the AGR. The sum total of all these tensions has been a series of rows between the CEGB and NNC,[39] and within the NNC itself.[40] At the time of writing the balance of advantage rests with the PWR lobby which has one of its most fervent supporters, Sir Walter Marshall, installed in the key position at the head of the CEGB and the balance was further tipped in their direction in May 1985 when it was announced that the NNC and Westinghouse were to set up a joint company to develop the British PWR on a highly commercial, fixed-price contract basis. However, the possibility of further setbacks inspired from within the industry cannot be ruled out.

The crucial point in this brief survey of the UK reactor programmes is that nuclear power decisions have not been taken on the basis of future energy needs. When British nuclear policy is placed in its global context, it becomes clear that it has been dictated primarily by the pressures of capitalist competition and growth, by the pursuit of corporate profitability and by changing conditions on the world nuclear market. It is difficult to see how reactor orders can be intended to meet a genuine need when overcapacity in the electricity grid already stands at 28 per cent[41] and when coal-fired power stations and coal-mines are being shut down ahead of their natural retirement dates.[42] The strategy has nothing to do with energy need but is rather a corporate and political strategy to favour nuclear power at the expense of coal and to satisfy the ambitions of GEC and the global export strategy of Westinghouse.

Nuclear technology is extremely complex, implying long periods of research and development work, long-term engineering contracts and the commitment of billions of pounds on the basis of guesses as to future rates of electricity demand and economic activity. As was made clear above, the current problems of the West's reactor suppliers stem from industrial overcapacity, built up as a result of past guesses which turned out to be wrong. However, the impact of this overcapacity, and of the general slowdown in reactor orders, goes much wider than the reactor-building companies themselves. It feeds right through the so-called 'nuclear fuel cycle' creating uncertainty and sharpening conflicts at every stage. Once again, British developments in these other areas of nuclear activity is best understood when placed in a wider context.

Uranium supply

The fuel for most nuclear reactors is uranium, a heavy element whose unstable atomic structure lends itself to the process of nuclear fission. World uranium supply now, and for the foreseeable future, is dominated by the reserves of just four countries: Canada, the USA, Namibia and Australia. In the 1940s and 1950s uranium was assumed to be geologically rare, but by the late 1960s it had become evident that it was in fact plentiful. As a result two things happened: the price fell, and big companies moved into it as a long-term investment on the reasonable calculation that the widely expected expansion of nuclear power would generate a steady demand and pull the price back up. The large oil companies were among the leaders in this trend and by the late 1960s owned 45 per cent of US reserves.[43] Other firms were also getting involved, however, including the British mining multinational, Rio Tinto Zinc (RTZ), which bought into the commodity on the private advice of British civil servants.[44]

By the early 1970s the uranium mining industry was dominated by a relatively small number of governments and companies, a situation lending itself to cartelization. A cartel did indeed develop and operated effectively from 1972 to 1974 to keep the price up.[45] From 1974 it was no longer necessary, as the first oil shock focused market attention on uranium as an alternative fuel source to oil. The price rose steadily to peak in 1976; and it seemed that the long-term strategy adopted by the oil and mining firms in the 1960s had paid off.

The US nuclear programme had of course started to falter before the price of uranium even reached its peak – an apparent contradiction which is explained by the fact that most uranium is supplied on long-term contracts at agreed prices, so that changing conditions can take a long while to feed through. This contractual situation was exacerbated by the determination of the uranium companies to press ahead with new investment and expansion of production on the continued expectation of a new upturn in reactor building. The upturn did not occur, so that from 1980 the market has faced a situation of chronic overproduction. It is generally agreed that two years' forward supply represents an ample level of stockpiling, but world stockpiles are now the equivalent of three, four or even six years' supplies.[46]

Nevertheless, British companies have done well out of uranium, despite the worsening market conditions. RTZ has supplied much of the UK's uranium requirements, civil and military, on a long-term contract from the Rossing mine in Namibia, in which it is the majority shareholder. Rossing's contribution to RTZ's overall profits has been as high as 13 per cent.[47] However, it is operated in direct contravention of rulings from the UN and the International Court of Justice,[48,49] because of the continuing South African occupation of Namibia. The Rossing contract has not been renewed, and supplies will apparently cease in the mid-1980s, although it has been suggested that Rossing might still provide uranium for the Trident nuclear missile programme.

The end of this contract will not mean an end to profitable British involvement in uranium mining. The result of the current world glut is not to stop mining altogether – too much has been invested for that – but to shift the balance of production from high-cost mines (mainly in the USA) to low-cost mines (mainly in Canada and Australia). In Canada, rich new reserves have been discovered in Saskatchewan, but 60 per cent of production is still from the enormous deposits in the Elliot Lake area, and production could continue here for decades to come. Mining at Elliot Lake is carried out by RTZ through its Canadian subsidiary Rio Algom.[50]

Meanwhile, the major new Australian development is at Roxby Downs where extensive uranium deposits occur alongside other minerals, including gold. The decision on whether to develop the Roxby Downs site split the Australian Labour Party in two and led to resignations from the government, but the leadership is committed to go ahead. Once again, UK capital is well represented: in 1983 the oil giant BP owned 49 per cent of the Roxby Downs project.[51]

The world uranium industry is therefore in a weak state, but despite this there are points of possible growth where extensive reserves exist which can be exploited at low cost. British multinational companies are strategically placed to make the most of these growth points. Furthermore, these multinationals are powerful enough in their own right to be able to influence government nuclear policy when necessary. BP is by far the biggest company in the country, RTZ has directors from all political parties, close links with the nuclear industry through its current Chief Executive (Sir Alastair Frame, formerly of the UKAEA); and close links with the City through its current Chairman (Sir Anthony Tuke, formerly of Barclays Bank). Continued nuclear expansion in Britain may therefore be motivated, at least in part, by the need to justify these corporations' uranium investments in Canada and Australia.

Uranium enrichment

The process of enrichment – bringing uranium fuel up to the necessary level of purity – is essential to the nuclear industry, but it is complex, costly and can consume enormous amounts of energy. Until the 1970s, the USA monopolized world supplies of enriched uranium and used this advantage to sell its reactors abroad by promising long-term fuel supply contracts. However, as part of the trend of establishing independent European nuclear industries, new enrichment consortia were set up on a multinational basis, to rival the USA. France established Eurodif together with Belgium, Italy, Spain and, briefly, Iran. Meanwhile the Netherlands, UK and West Germany joined forces to set up URENCO in 1971. The European consortia were at an advantage over the USA, in that they were able to exploit the new centrifuge enrichment technique which is much cheaper than the old gas-diffusion method. When the USA's gas-diffusion plant at Oak Ridge is in full operation, its power requirements are equivalent to those of a small city, or to the output of two large power stations.[52] The centrifuge method, however, requires only one-tenth as much power as gas diffusion.

Nevertheless, the new European enrichment capacity has come on stream at a difficult time. Once again, investment in new facilities was made on the expectation of a rapid expansion of nuclear power, which has not in fact occurred. Large-scale production still takes place in the USA, and in addition to this there are commercially available enrichment services from the USSR, new facilities in South Africa and Pakistan, and possible developments in Brazil, India and Taiwan. There is therefore considerable overcapacity in enrichment facilities, just as there is in uranium supply, and the result is an increasingly competitive international market.

Within this market, URENCO and Eurodif are tending to win business away from both the USA and USSR.[53] The British partner in URENCO is British Nuclear Fuels Ltd (BNFL), which manages one of the consortium's three centrifuge plants, at Capenhurst. Enrichment contracts at Capenhurst were worth $600 million in 1983.[54] However, the impact of overcapacity is felt in the trend to shorter-term contracts so that successful agreements no longer spell out a guaranteed long-term future.

As with uranium, Britain appears to be relatively well placed given the generally unfavourable market conditions. BNFL's stake in URENCO offers the opportunity of sharing in a growing business, if URENCO can continue to take contracts from the USA and if world nuclear orders hold steady or resume their expansion. However, the market will continue to be highly competitive and this opens up other frightening possibilities. It only takes 25 per cent as much work to produce bomb-grade enriched uranium from reactor-grade as it takes to produce reactor-grade from natural uranium.[55] It is therefore quite possible that enrichment corporations will be tempted to offer bomb-grade uranium to potential customers as an extra inducement in landing contracts. The very nature of nuclear technology, in which the civil and military are inextricably linked, lends itself to such arrangements – and deals of this sort may, indeed, already have occurred.[56] The current, highly competitive nature of the enrichment market can only increase the pressure for further similar deals.

Reprocessing and the fast breeder reactor

If the enrichment market has seen a European challenge to the USA, then this is even more the case in reprocessing. Reprocessing is a chemical process which separates out reuseable uranium and plutonium from unusable radioactive wastes. The uranium is converted back into fuel. The plutonium is stored for future use in fast breeder reactors, or is diverted to the nuclear weapons programme. The waste is dumped or stored, pending a more satisfactory solution.

The USA set its face against reprocessing in the mid-1970s, employing high-sounding rhetoric about preventing the proliferation of nuclear weapons. Reprocessing does indeed increase the risk of proliferation – but to many outside the USA it appeared that the rhetoric was no more than a smoke screen intended to defend the USA's weakening grip on nuclear fuel supply and to prevent the development of a line of nuclear technology in which it was already far behind the UK and France. Both of these countries had established reprocessing capacity precisely in order to achieve greater independence in fuel supply and in order to build up plutonium stocks for military purposes and future fast breeder reactor programmes.

The rationale behind reprocessing is inseparable from the fast breeder reactor. The fast breeder reactor or fast reactor is the last word in fission technology: in theory, it is possible for it to produce more fuel than it consumes, by using a fuel mixture of plutonium (recovered through reprocessing) and uranium-238. The advantage of this, from a nuclear engineer's point of view, is that uranium-238 is relatively plentiful, but it cannot be used as fuel for thermal reactors: they require the richer, but rarer isotope, uranium-235. The energy potential of the world's uranium reserves would thus be increased many times over,[57] *if* the theory of the fast reactor can be made a reality; if reprocessing can be made to work reliably enough to produce the necessary plutonium, and if plutonium can be constantly shuffled between fast reactors and reprocessing plant without leak, loss or theft. In Britain, the first fast reactor was commissioned at Dounreay in Scotland in 1959 and a prototype fast reactor started operating in the early 1970s at the same site.

The UK's reprocessing plant, which recovers both plutonium and reusable uranium, is at Sellafield (Windscale) in Cumbria, and is run by BNFL. At present, Sellafield only reprocesses fuel from the old Magnox reactors, and cannot deal with more modern types. A new facility is therefore being built, known as the Thermal Oxide Reprocessing Plant (THORP), which will handle oxide wastes from British AGRs and from foreign PWRs whose waste is accepted on contract. The latest estimate is that THORP, which will have a lifetime of about ten years, will cost $1.3 billion to build – and it has already attracted $2 billion worth of forward orders from abroad.[58] The expectation is that THORP will process an average of 600 tonnes per year, though it is designed to take, 1,200 tonnes.[59] However, even 600 tonnes is an optimistic target, given that the only operating oxide reprocessing plant in the world, at Cap La Hague in France, has experienced major technical problems and has found difficulty in honouring its contracts.[60]

BNFL frequently points to a healthy-looking log of forward orders and has even volunteered itself as a prime candidate for privatization.[61] However, a more sober look reveals that the reprocessing project, and the fast reactor programme to which it is linked, are in a fragile state. The depressed state of the world nuclear industry and uranium market affects this area, as it affects others. Reprocessing and the fast reactor only make commercial sense in the context of high uranium prices and relatively scarce uranium supplies. Reprocessing and fast reactor technologies are enormously complex and costly and the major justification for this capital investment is that they economize on fuel. If there is no fuel shortage, then the energy rationale for these technologies disappears, though a military rationale may still remain. It is highly significant that the THORP project was finally approved at the long-running Windscale Inquiry of 1977 on explicitly non-economic grounds, on the argument that their case was based on grounds of 'energy conservation'. This appears to suggest that considerations other than energy supply were at stake.[62]

On top of any possible military implications, the sheer size and momentum of these projects have become factors in their own right. Too much has already been invested, in both reprocessing and the fast reactor for the agencies concerned to pull out now. The construction of THORP therefore proceeds, even though its overt rationale has been undermined by uranium overproduction, even though the costs of reprocessing are rising and making it even more unattractive, and even though there appear to be major technical problems in oxide reprocessing.

The fast reactor programme is being kept alive by spreading the load. France is by far the most advanced country in this field, with an operational commercial-sized fast reactor, Superphenix, at Creys-Malville. The independent British programme was cut back in December 1982, but in August 1983 it was announced that the UK was joining a six-nation European collaborative programme. This is inevitably led by France but Britain is the next in line and has valuable technical experience to contribute especially in the area of reprocessing Fast Reactor fuel. In May 1985, the government announced plans to build a new reprocessing facility at Dounreay, next to Britain's prototype fast reactor but five times larger than the existing plant. This project represents the UK's contribution to the West European fast reactor programme.

Reprocessing and the fast reactor are essentially strategic technologies: they appear to hold out the promise of energy independence (though this argument is increasingly difficult to sustain) and they have a military function. They are also technologies which have developed their own momentum, so that governments are unwilling to abandon them when so much has already been invested. Market conditions make it unlikely that they will be profitable in any conventional sense of the word in the foreseeable future – but they offer non-commercial advantages which governments are prepared to pay for. It is even more unlikely that these activities will be privatized. The economic logic of reprocessing and the Fast Reactor is not market-dependent: it is a political logic moulded by state policy and state intervention.[64]

Waste disposal: the challenge to reprocessing

The aspect of nuclear power which has most caught the public imagination and aroused public fears is nuclear waste. All industrial processes generate waste products, but arguably none are as poisonous or as long-lived as those emerging from the process of nuclear fission. In a generally sluggish nuclear market, as explained above, there is less justification for economizing on uranium through reprocessing and a fast reactor programme. This means that unprocessed nuclear waste – including unused enriched uranium and fission products such as plutonium – must be disposed of in some other way. Storage is becoming increasingly popular as a medium-term or permanent 'solution' to the problem of nuclear waste and as a viable alternative to the option of reprocessing.

In Britain, nuclear waste at present finishes up at one of two sites, both of which are managed by BNFL: Windscale, or Drigg, in Cumbria. Until 1983 so-called 'low-level' waste was disposed of at sea but at the time of writing this has been halted, and is now under review (see p.143). Drigg has for years been used as a burial site for 'intermediate' level wastes and by 1984 was practically full. In that year, investigations started into two alternative sites for 'low' and 'intermediate' level disposal: a clay site at Bedford and a disused anhydrite mine at Billingham in Cleveland. At both these sites, there was immediate and vociferous public opposition to the industry's proposals and the Billingham option was dropped in 1985. 'High-level' wastes, the most virulent and long-lived forms, are currently stored at Windscale. The long-term intention is to transform this into a glass-like substance, a process known as vitrification, and then bury it deep underground.[65] All of these disposal arrangements are being made without any clear knowledge of their possible long-term impact on the environment, and without any guarantee against radioactive pollutants finding their way back to humanity through natural or biological pathways.

It is clear that long-term nuclear waste storage is going to expand in the years ahead. The CEGB itself, alarmed at the escalating costs of reprocessing, is considering long-term storage as a preferable option.[66] The result is that nuclear waste storage services are increasingly taking on a commercial aspect with the development of markets at both national and international levels.

In the UK, the civil engineering firm Wimpey has linked up

with a US partner to form Wimpey-Gilbert, specializing in nuclear waste techniques.[67] NEI, already involved in reactor building, has moved into the field by setting up NEI Waste Technologies with partners from the USA and Britain.[68] However, given the acute political sensitivity of the nuclear waste issue, it may become attractive for Western governments to sidestep the problem altogether by exporting it. Offers to receive Western wastes have come from Egypt, Argentina, China, the USSR and, more tentatively, from Australia.[69]

The overall picture is therefore of a developing market for nuclear waste disposal technologies and sites, a market which is developing precisely because of the weaknesses of the nuclear market more generally and because of the strains this places on the reprocessing option. This is not to suggest that nuclear waste storage will entirely replace reprocessing – as was stressed above, reprocessing has a strategic value which will attract continued state funding. However, utilities may be increasingly reluctant to pay for reprocessing costs and opt instead for waste storage. The two alternatives may therefore both continue, one subsidized by the state and the other on an increasingly commercial basis.

The appearance of an international market in nuclear waste disposal has serious implications for the environment and nuclear weapons proliferation, similar to those posed by the increasingly competitive market in enrichment services (see p.36). It will be in the interests of the recipient country to store its imported wastes as cheaply as possible – with the implication that they may be stored insecurely. Similarly, it will be in the interests of the donor country to avoid scandal and the asking of potentially awkward questions about the treatment of its radioactive exports. The scene will be set for a possibly disastrous conspiracy of silence.

Conclusions: the UK and the world market

Certain broad lessons emerge from these surveys of the British oil and nuclear industries. Firstly, it is clear that energy policy is not shaped by rational debate in Westminster or Whitehall, though these may officially be the seats of decision-making.

Policy is formed not only by British governments or public energy corporations but also by the strategies of private energy companies and by foreign state powers, all operating within the framework of constantly shifting world energy markets. UK energy policy only starts to make sense when it is placed in the context of this global struggle for power and profit. More specifically, it only starts to make sense when the historical role of the USA is appreciated.

In both the oil and nuclear sectors, British policy decisions since the Second World War have been subject to a tension between national independence and subservience to a world market dominated by the USA. As both industries have come to operate increasingly on a global scale, however, the option of narrow national independence has ceased to exist, and the pressures to fall in with world market trends have increased. In the case of nuclear power, this has meant falling in with the US nuclear corporations. Oil is more complex because the UK has become a major producer in precisely the period when the largely US-based oil companies were losing ground to the oil-producing states. The present Tory government has effectively taken the course of least resistance in both cases, given the prevailing global conditions; it has chosen to co-operate directly with the still-dominant US nuclear corporation, and it has chosen to take short-term advantage of the post-OPEC regime in the world oil industry.

The point of analysing the past is to help identify opportunities for the future. In both oil and nuclear power, Britain will continue to be a significant force for the foreseeable future: in oil not only because of North Sea reserves but also because of the activities of BP, Shell and Britoil; in nuclear power because of strategic involvement in uranium reserves, enrichment, reprocessing and the fast reactor. The UK is thus well placed to contribute to new initiatives in both these world industries. It could contribute to a restructuring of the world oil industry, in favour of those Third World countries for which oil is a vital necessity; and it could contribute to a scaling down and ultimate phasing out of nuclear activities on an international level. These are major and very long-term questions and more detailed proposals are discussed later (see p.165). However, it is important to establish here that the main point in analysing global pressures on UK energy policy under capitalism is to help identify some of the global opportunities which would be opened up by the introduction of a socialist energy strategy in the UK.

3. Britain's energy resources

Any understanding of the overall direction of British energy policy and of the energy options open in the years ahead must take into account certain factual realities. Fuel reserves are finite and can only be exploited at a certain rate; energy technologies have their limitations and further development requires policy decisions on investment; patterns of energy consumption must be taken into account and can only be gradually altered if socially damaging disruption is to be avoided. Furthermore, on the supply side, the contributions of different energy technologies cannot simply be added together as if any one technology could coexist with any other. In the real world, *some* energy choices tend to complement each other while others are mutually antagonistic or exclusive. This is because they are competing for scarce resources and markets and because they are all subject to their own economies of scale.

The issue becomes even more complicated when it is appreciated that the 'facts' on energy supply and consumption are subject to constant manipulation for commercial and political reasons. A good example is provided by the Sleipner story. In the early 1980s the British government agreed, in principle, to purchase large quantities of natural gas from Norway's North Sea Sleipner field. This was to make up an expected short-fall in UK gas supply in the 1990s which was predicted by the British Gas Corporation (BGC). The deal was opposed, however, by private oil companies engaged in gas production in the British sector of the North Sea: they felt that the Sleipner contract would put their customer, the BGC, in an unacceptably strong bargaining position and would force down their own prices.

The argument went on through 1983 and 1984 with each side

producing its own estimates of North Sea gas reserves and production forecasts to back up its own case. The BGC was ranged against most of the private oil companies, except for Esso – which had a 10 per cent stake in the Sleipner field and therefore had a good commercial reason for agreeing with the nationalized gas concern and opposing its colleagues in the private sector. In the end the government changed its mind and came down on the side of the majority of oil companies by cancelling the contract.

What emerges from this is that our knowledge about fuel reserves, or about the potential of a particular energy technology, does not exist in the abstract. It only comes into existence within a preexisting commercial and political context. Fuel reserves may be located by exploratory drilling or a new technique may unfold as a result of a research and development programme – but that drilling or that programme require the *prior* allocation of resources and expertise. Our knowledge about energy options is therefore dependent on and structured by the commercial and political judgements of private capital and the state.

This does not mean that it is impossible to make a simple factual statement. It *does* mean that factual statements must be treated with care and that apparently dry, technical or statistical data must be placed in their proper political context.

Within these limitations, the present chapter is intended to sketch out the factual and statistical background to various debates in British energy policy.

Patterns of energy consumption

The broad trend in UK energy consumption over the past ten to fifteen years is easily summarized. Overall it has fallen: primary energy consumption in 1983 was 11 per cent down on 1973.[1] Within this smaller total, coal consumption held relatively steady from 1973, following its long decline in the 1950s and 1960s, until a new decline set in from 1980.[2] Oil consumption peaked around 1973 and declined noticeably in the mid-1970s, and again from 1980.[3] Natural gas consumption rose spectacularly from nowhere throughout the 1970s, so that by 1982 it supplied 28 per cent of primary energy demand.[4] Nuclear power expanded but far more slowly than had been planned, and in 1982 it, together with hydroelectric power, still met less than 6 per cent of primary energy needs.[5] A slow decline in coal and oil, a slow expansion of nuclear power, and a rapid expansion of gas, are the main features of recent years – all of these occurring in the context of an overall fall in energy consumption which in itself is unique in postwar history.

Primary energy figures relate to the initial fuel input: it is important to look also at the other end of the process, the forms in which energy is delivered to the consumer. There is great variation in the thermodynamic efficiency of different fuels and energy processes, so that the pattern of final demand can look very different from the pattern of primary energy inputs. Yet it is the form in which energy is delivered which is all-important to the user.

Just as the structure of primary energy consumption changed in the 1970s, so too did the pattern of final energy demand. Solid fuel consumption plummeted and oil demand fell, both of them seeing traditional markets seized by the advent of cheap natural gas. The amount of energy delivered as electricity also rose steadily and this, coupled with the collapse of the solid fuel market, meant that the coal industry became increasingly tied to the single function of electricity generation.[6]

These are some of the bare figures, but in themselves they tell us little about the relationship between energy supply and broader social and economic trends. The first, crucial question concerns the overall fall in energy demand between the early 1970s and early 1980s. This decline does reflect greater attention to conservation, a greater degree of energy awareness as a result of the oil shocks – but much more importantly, it reflects the collapse of whole sectors of manufacturing industry and the restructuring of the national economy. In 1973 iron, steel and other industries accounted for 42 per cent of all energy consumption; by 1983 they represented only 31 per cent within a reduced overall figure.[7] Meanwhile, the domestic, road transport and 'miscellaneous' (mostly private services) sectors had all increased their shares, both relatively and absolutely.[8] The overall fall in energy consumption is therefore related to a major shift in the balance of the economy, away from relatively energy-intensive manufacturing activity and towards less energy-intensive service and domestic use.

What follows from this is that any projections of future energy use must be related to future economic strategy and economic trends. Energy options must be chosen with these wider priorities in mind: if, for example, reindustrialization is regarded as an important economic goal, then the energy consequences of reindustrialization must be taken into account. Conversely, if the trend towards a service economy is welcomed because of its low energy-intensiveness, then the political and social consequences of a service economy must also be taken on board (see p.153).

The sections which follow are intended to map out the parameters within which these choices must be made in the next few decades.

Fossil fuel resources

Britain is exceptionally fortunate in its fossil fuel resources. It has coal enough for centuries and oil and gas enough for decades to come. These reserves will however, only play a constructive part in the country's future if they are treated with care. If they are regarded purely as market commodities with long-term investment decisions dictated by short-term price signals, then reserves may be wasted and opportunities lost.

Coal provides the best example. Nationalized in 1947, the industry has had its ups and downs (see p.133). In 1974 the new 'Plan for Coal' inaugurated an expansionist policy both in terms of production targets (170 million tonnes by the year 2,000) and investment in new capacity. What has happened in practice is that investment in new capacity *has* gone ahead, but the argument of a 'shrinking market' has been used by the National Coal Board so that this new capacity comes to replace existing capacity since productivity (and therefore 'profitability') in new pits is clearly higher than in old. This is the heart of the debate about 'uneconomic pits' which sparked the 1984-5 strike: 'uneconomic' pits are made to look 'uneconomic' precisely as a result of NCB investment decisions. The single biggest new pit coming on stream is Selby, with projected production of 25 million tonnes per year. If 25 million tonnes of existing 'uneconomic' capacity is to be lost in order to make way for Selby – and this is the logic of the NCB's position – then 69 pits must close with a net job loss of 63,000.[9]

The loss of coal's previous domestic and transport markets means that it is now overwhelmingly tied to electricity generation – and its market is also shrinking here, as a result of a consistent CEGB commitment to build oil-fired and nuclear, rather than coal-fired, power stations since the 1960s.

There is nothing inevitable about the expansion of oil and nuclear power in electricity supply at coal's expense. Furthermore, (see p.8) world trade in coal is expanding fast and will continue to do so into the next century, so that export markets should be a real possibility, especially the export of low-sulphur Scottish and Welsh coal to Western Europe as part of the European effort to reduce acid-rain emissions. There is no shortage of uses for coal, there is no shortage of technical options for using it cleanly and effectively, and there is certainly no shortage of coal itself – UK reserves are estimated at 45 billion tonnes, or enough for nearly 400 years at current rates of consumption.[10] The current contraction of the coal industry reflects political priorities (see p.83) and has nothing to do with the potential of the industry itself.

North Sea oil provides a stark contrast to the coal industry. With coal we have an energy resource which can last for centuries but which is being run down; with oil we have a resource which is known to be finite and relatively short-term, yet it is being developed as fast as possible. The development of the British oil industry is discussed elsewhere (see p.19); here the emphasis is upon patterns of consumption and supply.

Transport, and especially road transport, has always been the crucial component in oil consumption, but the 'cheap oil' era of the 1950s and 1960s saw consumption spread throughout the economy. Since the 1973 oil shock these other sectors have reduced their oil consumption though it has continued to rise in the transport sector, contributing to the problem of acid rain.

The UK is the fifth largest oil producer in the world and a significant force in world export markets: by the mid-1980s about 40 per cent of net production was exported, the main markets being the USA and Western Europe. The mid-1980s also see North Sea production at its peak. From about 1986 it will decline, not because the oil is running out but because many of the largest and most accessible fields have already been exploited. As production moves north and west to smaller and more difficult fields, output will necessarily fall.

At the time of writing, in 1985, oil reserves are estimated to be between 1,408 and 5,278 million tonnes, (about 2,155-8075 million tonnes of coal equivalent or mtce).[11] In theory, if the upper figure turns out to be correct, Britain could continue to produce at present levels to about 2030. In reality, as stressed above, production levels are determined by accessibility and distribution of reserves, and the mere fact that reserves exist does not alter the likelihood of the UK becoming a net importer again in the 1990s, largely due to the high production levels maintained in those 'golden years' of the 1980s.

With natural gas, it is generally expected that the UK will start importing on a large scale in the 1990s. The use of gas has expanded massively over the last 15 years, penetrating just about every available market. From meeting 5 per cent of final energy demand in 1960, it rose to supply 27 per cent in 1980, and in the process came to meet 53 per cent of domestic energy requirements and 25 per cent of industry's needs.[12]

UK gas reserves are estimated at between 899 and 2,259 billion cubic metres,[13] (about 1,215-3050 mtce). In the early 1980s total gas consumption was running at about 72 mtce, of which about 16 mtce was being imported.[14] The Department of Energy regards it as a possibility that consumption could still be at that level in 2000, but falling domestic production would by then mean imports of about 23 mtce.[15] The general expectation is that the UK will be importing significant quantities of natural gas in the 1990s, or looking for alternatives, such as synthetic natural gas, derived from coal, to supplement continued production from the North Sea.

Conservation and combined heat and power

To look at fuel reserves is an important part of the energy picture, but it is only one part. Enormous scope exists for saving
energy which at present is wasted, and the introduction of conservation measures can obviously have a major impact on the
rate at which finite fuel reserves are consumed.

The areas of conservation with which most people are familiar
are loft insulation, hot-water tank jackets and double glazing.
Around 90 per cent of homes now have tank insulation, and
about 80 per cent have some loft insulation.[16] However, the
greatest take-up tends to be in higher-income groups.

The government has calculated that the full 'economic' potential for domestic sector insulation investment is around £3 billion
(1981 prices).[17] This investment would save around 2 billion
therms per year – or nearly 2 per cent of primary energy consumption, and this is after taking into account the fact that most
of this energy-saving potential is to be found in lower-income
groups, where some of the benefits would be taken in the form of
improved levels of heating.

Within the industrial and commercial sectors, similar scope
exists. One study[18] calculates that energy consumption per unit
of output could be reduced by 30 per cent in the steel industry, 33
per cent in engineering, 24 per cent in chemicals and so on. However, all of these savings require *investment* in new machinery,
new techniques, new plant and buildings. Conservation is not
merely a matter of patching up the leaks in the fabric of the
economy, it is a matter of constructing a new energy-conscious
fabric.

In this context, it worth looking at combined heat and power
(CHP). CHP is not generally regarded as a conservation measure, but it does, nevertheless, save significant amounts of
energy. In a conventional power station much heat is produced
which simply goes to waste: for every 100 tonnes of coal burned,
the heat equivalent of 60-70 tonnes disappears up cooling towers,
into rivers, or during conversion. CHP puts much of this waste
heat to work, using it to heat water which can then be supplied to
local homes, offices or factories in a district heating (DH)

scheme. The laying down of new water pipes can be a costly exercise, but once installed, a CHP-DH system more than doubles power station efficiency and creates a local source of energy ideally suited to the basic task of space and water heating. With new coal-burning technologies also installed – such as pressurized fluidized-bed combustion, which extracts more of the coal's energy, efficiency rises yet again.

CHP's institutional problem is that, unlike gas and electricity, there is no statutory body in existence to promote its use. Current government policy is to encourage local schemes but only if they can raise private finance.

Renewable energy sources

The 'renewables' are those energy technologies which tap natural processes on and around the earth, rather than mining and burning finite energy resources. Of these natural processes by far the most important is the regular arrival of solar radiation, together with all the consequences of its arrival: condensation and convection, wind patterns and photosynthesis. The gravitational pull between the earth and moon is also important in generating tidal movements. Geothermal energy, tapping the geologically stored heat of the planet, is also usually counted as a renewable, though technically it is a finite energy resource.

At the time of writing, government funding for *all* the renewable energy technologies stands at about £14 million per annum, and is expected to stay at that level for the next few years.[19]

The most direct form of renewable energy is the tapping of the power of the sun, whether through passive heating (soaking up the solar radiation through careful architectural and design arrangements); solar collectors (devices which provide space or water heating from the sun's warmth); or solar cells (which convert sunlight to electricity by means, for example, of a silicon semiconductor). There are widely differing estimates of the contribution which solar energy might ultimately make to the UK's energy needs: in the late 1970s the Energy Commission suggested a solar contribution equivalent to 5 mtce by 2000, or 1.5 per cent of primary energy consumption,[20] while the UK section of the International Solar Energy Society suggested 35 mtce by 2020, or 11 per cent.[21] A report produced for the Commission of the European Communities concluded that solar energy could provide over 73 mtce in Western Europe by 2020[22] – and of this the UK would expect about 12 mtce, or 4 per cent of UK primary consumption given its share of European energy consumption.

When solar radiation reaches the earth it immediately launches numerous natural processes, including photosynthesis. The next renewable energy source to consider therefore is biomass, or the extraction of energy from organic materials including refuse, sewerage, straw, vegetable oils, wood and specially grown energy crops. In all cases, useful energy is obtained by burning or breaking down the vegetable matter so as to produce a solid, liquid or gaseous fuel. In Britain it has been estimated that biomass could ultimately contribute 23-30 mtce or 7-9 per cent of primary consumption, and this may understate its ultimate potential.[23]

Just as biomass is an organic byproduct of solar radiation, so wind energy is an atmospheric one, with major potential in Britain. This potential can be broken into two broad categories. At a local level, councils and other bodies can set up small wind turbines: this has already been done in many places, ranging from urban housing developments to isolated rural communities. Many of the research and industrial groupings working on wind energy consider that wind turbines in this range – about 100 to 300 kW – offer the best technical and economic prospects.

On a larger scale, the CEGB and some private engineering companies are experimenting with wind-turbines up to 4 MW in capacity. The CEGB has a 200 KW turbine at Carmarthen Bay, and in 1983 announced its intention to build a 4 MW machine at Richborough, Kent. Meanwhile a private consortium, the Wind Energy Group (comprising Taylor-Woodrow, British Aerospace and GEC) is working on a 3 MW turbine, following trials of its 250 KW turbine in Orkney.

It has been estimated that small-scale wind-energy schemes could contribute the equivalent of 5 to 10 mtce, or 3 per cent, to UK energy needs,[24] while an ultimate contribution equivalent to 92 mtce per annum, or 29 per cent of current primary consumption, might be expected.[25] Schemes on this scale might provide environmental problems, however, both in terms of unsightliness and from the noise generated by blades and turbines.

The action of the sun on the atmosphere causes wind currents and thus waves in the sea, creating a potential for wave energy. Wave power is a new idea and a range of devices have been tested in recent years, all of them seeking to turn wave motion into electricity. The main problem with all of them is how to make them robust enough to withstand constant battering and yet keep material costs down. Britain is exceptionally well-endowed with good sites for wave-power schemes: it has perhaps the best site in the world off the Western Isles and other excellent locations off the northeast Scottish coast and Land's End.

Major cuts in government funding from 1982 have restricted wave power's options, however. Work proceeds on small-scale machines, but there is no large development on the scale justified by Britain's potential. Ironically, Norway is now building the world's first major wave-power station, using technology pioneered in the UK. Nevertheless, the fact remains that Britain's annual wave-power potential may be equivalent to 120 mtce or 38 per cent of primary consumption.[26] Large wave-power projects would need to be sited so as not to interfere with shipping and to avoid environmental objections.

Tidal power might at first sight appear to be closely related to wave power. In fact its origins lie not in the action of the sun upon the earth, but in the gravitational attraction between the earth and the moon. As with wave power, however, technical development centres on the task of channelling water movement so as to convert its energy to electricity. In the UK, four sites have been identified which offer significant tidal-power potential: the Severn Estuary, Solway Firth, Morecambe Bay and the Wash.

At the time of writing, two schemes for a Severn tidal barrage have been put forward for consideration. The first, a massive structure costing £6 billion, could generate 7 GW or 12 mtce, equivalent to 6 per cent of electricity demand. However, it would also cause serious damage to the ecology of the Severn. The second, more modest scheme would generate less electricity, 1.05 GW or 2 mtce, but would also provide a road crossing of the estuary. The two schemes are backed by rival civil engineering firms.[27] Overall, it has been suggested that full development of tidal-power potential could provide the equivalent of 26 mtce per annum or 8 per cent of current primary consumption.[28]

Hydro power is the oldest renewable energy source: the English Industrial Revolution was based in the first instance on water mills and only subsequently on steam power. Today, hydro power is generally geared to electricity production, using turbines rather than mills. Britain is not particularly well endowed with good sites; if fully exploited, hydro power might contribute the equivalent of the current nuclear programme.

Installed capacity at present totals 2.3 GW or the equivalent of two large conventional power stations. Much of this capacity is in Scotland, and it contributes about 2 per cent of UK electricity. The scope for further large or medium-sized projects is certainly limited, though there are some possible sites in Scotland. However, there is much greater potential for small hydroschemes, with many rivers and streams in England and Wales which could also be tapped. Installations of 25 KW or less could be constructed in many places, either to generate electricity for the grid, or to be used locally, thus saving energy by avoiding the need to import electricity or other fuels.[29]

Finally, geothermal energy, which draws on the residual heat of certain rock formations, is a long-term resource, but a finite one. There are two sorts of geological formation which can be exploited in this way: deposits of hot underground water (aquifiers), and formations of hot dry rock. In the UK seven possible aquifier sites have been identified, with an energy potential running into hundreds of thousands of mtce. At the same time, tests in hot dry rock at Cambourne in Cornwall imply a potential in Cornwall alone of 8,000 mtce, or 25 times the UK's current annual primary energy consumption.[30] The significance of geothermal energy may, in the end, be enormous.

This necessarily brief survey of the renewable energy potential in Britain has ignored many crucial questions; not only technical problems concerning the efficient exploitation of these opportunities, but also environmental, social and economic implications. However, the single crucial point which does emerge is that there is an enormous potential in the renewables. Even experts from the Department of Energy and the CEGB admit that renewable energy sources could provide between 20 and 25 per cent of electricity needs by 2025-30.[31]

Electricity storage and supply

Many of the renewable energy sources – wind power, wave power, tidal power, hydro power, plus solar and geothermal energy in some circumstances – would produce useful energy in the form of electricity. This immediately poses a problem, in that the pattern of electricity supply from these sources would, by definition, be erratic, whereas consumers need to know that electricity will be available as they require it. Clearly, energy storage techniques are essential if the renewables are to be harnessed on a large scale.

At present the only large-scale forms of energy storage in the UK (apart from batteries or accumulators) are pumped water schemes operated by the electricity boards. During periods of low demand, surplus electricity is used to pump water from a low reservoir to a higher one; and during periods of high demand, the water is released to generate electricity as in a hydroelectric power station. When the massive Dinorwic pumped storage scheme is complete, British capacity will stand at around 2,600 MW – the equivalent to the output of two and a half large power stations.

Various other energy storage possibilities are being explored. Compressed air storage (in West Germany), flywheels (in Northern Ireland) and even large-scale batteries could all make a contribution. However, it needs to be said that due to the general low funding of new energy technologies, no work has yet been done on the precise mechanisms for linking renewable energy sources into storage systems. As with the renewables themselves, it is possible to point to a clear potential, but resources are insufficient for that potential to be precisely quantified.

This leads to the electricity supply system as a whole. Electricity is not a fuel: it is a secondary energy form, a convenient means of distributing and delivering energy which is *derived from* other fuels or sources. Its advantage is that it is a flexible 'common carrier', but its disadvantage is that the energy cost of converting primary fuel sources into electricity can be prohibitive. The electricity supply industry is in fact the highest *consumer* of primary energy in the country.[32] However, the fact remains that electricity is a flexible and unique energy form, indispensable to modern society, and the national grid which has been built up since the mid-1920s should be regarded as a prime social asset.

Electricity is uniquely useful for certain purposes: motor and mechanical tasks, lighting, electronics and communications. However, it has been used increasingly in recent years for tasks outside these categories, such as space heating, for which it is inappropriate and inefficient. The net result, when added to the inherent energy cost of electricity conversion, is that electricity supply consumes 32 per cent of all primary energy but only produces about 13 per cent of useful delivered energy.[33] These inefficiencies are exacerbated by the trend to install larger and larger generating sets in power stations, although the evidence suggest that the optimum size is in the 200-300 MW range.[34]

Precisely because electricity is a common carrier drawing upon all energy sectors, the structure of the electricity supply system has major implications for the structure of energy supply as a whole. It is therefore worth taking note of recent trends in the CEGB and SSEB systems. Between 1973 and 1983 overall electricity consumption fell. It declined especially sharply in the industrial sector, and less dramatically elsewhere, and these falls more than offset a spectacular increase in electricity consumption in the service sector, in shops and offices. Associated with this falling consumption has been a reduction in the installed capacity of the national grid. However, this small reduction in the capacity of power stations is associated with a major shift in the *type* of power stations. From the late 1960s, all orders for new power stations have been for oil-fired, nuclear, or gas-turbine stations, except for the single order for Drax B coal-fired station placed in 1977. Given that it can take a decade for a power station to be built, these ordering decisions are now bearing fruit. Between 1963 and 1972, nearly three-quarters of new capacity coming on stream was coal-fired; but between 1973 and 1982, only half such new capacity was coal-fired, while 24 per cent was oil-fired and 19 per cent nuclear. Of the capacity under construction in late 1983, 46 per cent was oil-fired, 38 per cent nuclear and only 16 per cent coal-fired.[35] The trend in electricity supply, away from coal and towards oil and nuclear, could not be clearer.

Nuclear power

Nuclear power requires separate discussion, not only because it is the most controversial energy source, but because it is unique in its operations and implications. Like the fossil fuel industries, it derives energy from a finite mineral source – but unlike them, it breaks down that mineral's atomic structure rather than simply indulging in chemical combustion. Like some renewables, it generally delivers useful energy as electricity – but unlike them, it implies a highly centralized system dependent on a few massive power stations, rather than a decentralized system with a range of local inputs. Nuclear power stations can also deliver energy as heat in addition to electricity, in the form of nuclear combined heat and power (CHP). However, the economics of CHP means that heat-supplying nuclear power stations must be in or very close to the urban-industrial areas they serve, which poses extra radiation dangers. So far nuclear CHP has only been developed in the USSR. Finally, nuclear power stations produce pollutants and byproducts which are unique in the degree and longevity of the hazards they present.

The development of nuclear power in Britain is dealt with elsewhere (see p.25) and the steadily increasing importance of nuclear power within the electricity supply system has already been stressed. The technology developed so far has been based on nuclear fission harnessing the energy released when atoms of uranium-235, or some other suitable element, are split. Research is proceeding into other nuclear technologies, which may provide more energy than basic nuclear fission. The first of these is the fast reactor, popularly known as the 'fast breeder', discussed on pp.37-39 above.

The other new nuclear technology is Fusion, in which energy is released by fusing two very light nuclei. If it works, it could in theory provide almost limitless, relatively clean energy for centuries to come. No mining would be necessary: the fuel would simply be water which is the most obvious source of deuterium nuclei for the fusion process itself. However, the theoretical promises are reminiscent of the claims once made for nuclear fission. The practice is rather different.

First, there is an enormous complex engineering problem in creating the conditions for nuclear fusion to occur in a predictable and controllable way. Despite millions of pounds invested by the EEC and the USSR, the only fusion power achieved so far is the hydrogen bomb, and it is important to remember that fusion is as much a spin-off of the nuclear weapons programme as is fission. Second, there is no guarantee that fusion would be clean: one of its byproducts is tritium, which is highly radioactive and also a central ingredient in the hydrogen bomb. The promise of limitless energy held out by nuclear fusion is therefore highly speculative and highly dubious.

Nuclear power currently provides about 16 per cent of electricity demand and 5 per cent of total primary energy requirements. In its evidence to the Sizewell Inquiry, the Department of Energy presented a range of economic and energy options for the future, but in all of them nuclear power was assumed to expand dramatically. By 2010, the Department expects it to be contributing 60-68 per cent of electricity demand, and 20-28 per cent of primary energy needs.[36] A commercial fast reactor might just be coming on stream in the UK by 2010, but the vast bulk of this projected nuclear electricity would be generated by conventional fission reactors, both AGRs, ordered in the 1960s and 1970s, and PWRs, ordered in the 1980s and 1990s. A nuclear programme on this scale would inevitably present major problems of security and radioactive pollution.

Nuclear power stations are capable of delivering this much electricity in *technical* terms: the obstacles to such a programme, which might mean commissioning over 63GW of nuclear electricity between 1991 and 2010, will be economic, industrial and political.[37]

Conclusions

This has been an extremely brief survey of a very wide and complex subject. Many crucial issues have been ignored, particularly the social, political and economic implications of pursuing different energy options. This has been deliberate, precisely because the other chapters of the book look at these issues in far more detail. The intention here has simply been to create a sense of the technical and material parameters within which *any* energy policy making must take place in the next few decades.

The main problem with an exercise of this sort, as was made clear earlier in the chapter, is that it depends on intelligent guesswork about future developments, and since there is no shortage of pundits ready to put forward their own estimates, there is a problem of whom to trust. There is no easy solution to this situation. In order to present the data discussed above in an easily digestible form, while recognizing its tentative character, the tables below present a set of 'optimistic' estimates for each of the energy sources. These figures are not ours but are put forward by intelligent advocates of each of the sources.

The single crucial point which emerges is, quite simply, that Britain has more than enough energy for the foreseeable future. There need be no sense of crisis in determining energy priorities: instead, we have the space to identify the sort of policy we want in the light of our social and economic priorities.

The tables below do not represent forecasts and the figures given are not endorsed by the present authors. The tables are intended to give an idea of the range and scale of energy options open to the UK. The projections to the year 2000, 2010 or 'ultimate potential' are all relatively optimistic and are intended to convey the upper end of the potential of each resource.

One of the most detailed studies of the potential of energy conservation in the UK is that of the International Institute for Environment and Development (see p.103). In Table 3.1 below, its projections of primary energy consumption at 2000 and 2010 are compared with those of the Department of Energy (which assume conservation is left to 'market prices'), with various assumptions regarding economic growth.

Table 3.1. Conservation potential – primary energy consumption (Figures in mtce/p.a.)

	mtce 2000	2010
DEn: GDP growth ½ per cent p.a./high fuel prices	328[b]	328[b]
IIED: average GDP growth c. 1.8 per cent p.a.	330[a]	309[a]
IIED: average GDP growth c. 2.4 per cent p.a.	361[a]	357[a]
DEn: GDP growth 2½ per cent p.a./low fuel prices	461[b]	549[b]

Source: (a) Gerald Leach, *A Low Energy strategy for the UK*, London: Science Reviews Ltd, 1979. (b) DEn., *Proof of Evidence for the Sizewell 'B' Public Inquiry;* London: Department of Energy, 1982.

Table 3.2. Fossil fuels

	Coal	Oil	Gas
Remaining reserves (mtce)	45,000[a]	2,155-8,075[b]	1,215-3050[b]
Current rate of UK consumption (mtce/p.a.)	120[c]	138[c]	70[c]
Depletion period at current rates of consumption (years)	375	16-58	22-54
Possible level of UK production in 2000 (mtce/p.a.)	120[d]	88[e]	59[f]

Sources: (a) Gerald Foley, *The Energy Question*, Harmondsworth: Penguin, 1981, p. 113. (b) *Financial Times*, 9 May 1984. (c) HMSO, *Digest of UK Energy Statistics 1983, HMSO*, 1984. (d) DEn., *Proof of Evidence for the Sizewell 'B' Inquiry*, London: Department of Energy, 1982. (e) Gerald Leach, *A Low Energy Strategy for the UK*, London: Science Reviews Ltd, 1979. (f) *Financial Times*, 14 January 1985.

Table 3.3 Nuclear power
The main constraint on nuclear power generation is not the rate at which fuel resources can be made available, but the speed at which nuclear power stations can be built and brought on stream in the face of political, financial and technical obstacles.

Predicted level of nuclear power generation in 2000	*mtce*
	38-73

Source: DEn., *Proof of Evidence for the Sizewell 'B' Inquiry*, London: DEn., 1982.

Table 3.4 Renewables
Geothermal energy is often counted as a renewable though technically it is a finite resource. A geothermal contribution of 4 mtce/p.a. is thought possible by 2000, and reserves in Cornwall alone are thought to reach 8,000 mtce[b].

	Possible level of energy contribution in 2000 (mtce/p.a.)	Ultimate potential in UK (mtce/p.a.)
Solar	8[a]	35[a]
Wind	8[a]	92[b]
Wave	15[a]	120[a]
Tidal	10[a]	26[b]
Biomass	3[a]	30[b]
Hydro	2[a]	6[a]

Sources: (a) NATTA, *Alternative Technology, the Answer to the Energy Crisis?*, Milton Keynes, 1983. (b) Michael Flood, *Solar Prospects*, London: Wildwood House, 1983.

PART 2

4. The labour movement's record

In order to assess future possibilities it is useful to look back at the record of the Labour Party and the official trade union movement with respect to energy policy over the last decade.

Labour in government and the Labour Party

Labour was last in government from 1974-9. Labour's energy minister during all but the first year of this period was Tony Benn. Thus an assessment provides not only a reminder of Labour's performance in government, but also an indication of how the Left in the party have performed in office.

Energy policy in this period must be seen in relation to Labour's general economic and political record. Labour came to power in 1974 at the end of a period of exceptionally high trade union militancy. Millions during the previous four years had been involved in opposing the Heath government's Industrial Relations Act. Occupations in factories and other workplaces had become almost a common occurrence in response to threatened closures or redundancies and there had been a wave of strikes against the government's wages policy. The miners in particular had won an important victory in the 1972 strike, and in 1974 the miners' strike set the scene for the defeat of Heath's government.

Brought to power in this way by a relatively confident and militant working class, Labour did nothing to channel this confidence in a socialist direction. After an initial wages boom the Labour administration, led first by Wilson and later by Callaghan, joined with the trade union leadership to impose 'voluntary' wage restraints in the form of the social contract. Together with the high inflation that they were designed to combat, these restraints brought about the biggest fall in real wages ever seen in the twentieth century.[1] Finally the patience of significant groups of workers with the Labour-TUC alliance ran out and the winter of 1978-9 saw a series of bitter strikes in public services which were still fresh in the mind when Labour fought and lost the May 1979 election.

Labour failed in government either to advance the prospects for socialist development or even to manage capitalism success-fully. The collapse of the Callaghan government followed from a political and economic strategy reflecting the consensus view held by Labour and trade union leadership since the end of the Second World War. It had been assumed that capitalism could be managed successfully with the right approach to economic plan-ning by the state. Sustained economic growth would guarantee full employment and wealth for all and socialism would develop gradually through time as the inevitable expansion of wealth made inequalities irrelevant. Leaving aside the fundamental mis-take of equating socialism with a benevolent capitalism, this approach was by 1974 no longer in tune with economic reality. The world economy was in recession and in the advanced indust-rial countries unemployment and inflation were rising together. In the early 1970s commentators were forced to acknowledge the end of the Keynesian era of successful planning. It *was* the end of an era, the end of the prolonged postwar boom for the Western economies, but Labour in office after 1974, as in opposition from 1979, was unable to adjust and unable to provide an alternative.

Energy policy

Set against this gloomy background and against the continuing domination of energy policy by multinational companies and state monopolies, it is remarkable that Benn's energy policy managed to achieve anything at all. It must be remembered that it was in part a national and international energy crisis that brought Labour to power so that, for instance, Labour's much-vaunted programme of investment in the coal industry was only possible because, in the wake of the massive increases in interna-tional oil prices, coal mining on this scale was cost-competitive again for the first time since the late 1950s.[2]

Benn's period as Energy Secretary *did* stimulate serious

thought and planning at government level about long-term energy policy – and, when compared to the ad hoc approach adopted by British governments before and since, this must be held up as a major achievement. In 1976 and 1977 the Department of Energy published a discussion document and a policy review which both addressed long-term energy strategy.[3] 1976 also saw a major national energy conference and this in turn led to the creation of the Energy Commission which first met late in 1977. The role of the Energy Commission was to advise and assist the Department of Energy in the development of a national energy strategy. From its inception, until it was disbanded by the Thatcher administration, the commission produced a steady stream of energy papers relating to a wide range of issues in the energy debate. It was the early work of the Energy Commission which provided the basis of the government's 1978 Green Paper on Energy (which remains to this date the only green paper on energy ever produced by a British government).[4]

These are undoubtedly positive developments. However, both the Department of Energy Policy Review and the government green paper made estimates of future energy demand which, even at the time, seemed excessively high, placed a high emphasis on the nuclear option, and did not include renewable resources at all as a source of supply by the year 2000. (Both papers acknowledged that up to 40 million tonnes coal equivalent could potentially be supplied by renewables but discounted this in their final calculations.)

Taken as a whole, Labour's energy policy during this period can be seen to reflect the general emphasis of these papers, as follows.

Coal In coal mining Labour endorsed the NCB 'Plan for Coal' of 1974[5] which aimed to maintain total production at around 135 million tons per annum by 1985 and would require a £600 million programme of capital investment. This level of production was considerably lower than in the 1950s and 1960s, but nevertheless the increasing age of existing pits made a high commitment of investment essential to maintain it. Coal was to be ensured a safe future at the centre of any long-term energy strategy. Miners' wage settlements were more favourable than most under the

Labour administration, particularly the 'special case' settlements of 1974, but nevertheless over the five years of Labour government even miners' wages did not keep up with the general rate of inflation. Furthermore, on Benn's initiative, the miners became party to a productivity deal in 1978 which, by introducing wide variations in pay from pit to pit, has seriously damaged solidarity across the union.[6]

North Sea oil and gas   In 1973 the rate of return on capital for oil companies after tax on North Sea revenue was as high as 60 per cent in some instances, compared to only 8½-9 per cent for British manufacturing as a whole.[7] Prior to 1973 the government involvement had been largely limited to issuing production licences and leaving the oil companies to rake in the profits.

In 1974 the Department of Energy made a commitment to establish 'greater public control' of the North Sea deposits while also gaining a 'fair share of the profits to the nation'.[8] Labour embarked on a number of measures designed both to increase state participation in the industry, and to collect a higher proportion of the oil revenues as tax. A new national oil company – British National Oil Company (BNOC) – was set up in 1976 which would by 1981 have had a controlling stake in more than half of the oil production in the UK fields. Had these measures been allowed to develop, they might have checked the rapid depletion of North Sea resources and would have made available for better use a greater amount of the profits. Labour was clearly taking a step in the right direction. All of these measures have since been undone by the Thatcher government.

Nuclear power   Despite Benn's stated commitment to public debate and open government, and despite a public inquiry and a whole range of official reports and studies, the five years of nuclear policy from 1974-9 look much as though decisions were prompted most of all by institutional inertia.

Under Labour, nuclear power continued to be allocated the lion's share of research and development funding in the energy field: a major new development in the reprocessing industry was passed through parliament (Windscale); BNFL expanded its uranium enrichment facilities at Capenhurst; and through its role in URENCO continued to sell enriched uranium on the world market. The British multinational RTZ continued, with government support, to mine and sell more uranium than any other single company in the world and the thorny problem of what to do with nuclear waste remained unsolved. It is true that Benn fended off the powerful corporate lobby for a commitment to the PWR, but few would dispute now that the decision in 1978 to build two new AGRs, despite the manifest problems with the technology, was little more than a stopgap. Clearly Benn's strongest supporters in this were also the most immediate beneficiaries – the management and some of the unions in the power plant industry, and the research and design departments in the UKAEA.

Benn's struggle with the powerful lobby for the PWR has been well documented,[9] but it should also be remembered that he did not even attempt to break the domination of the energy field by the well established pro-nuclear lobbies in both the state and the private sector. Everything was left intact for the enthusiastically pro-nuclear Tory government to pick up the reins in 1979 and go ahead with plans for a fullscale PWR programme. If the programme falters now it will be largely because sufficient doubts have been raised about the safety of the PWR. It will not be because the previous Labour administration did anything positive to divert Britain from a nuclear future.

Finally, it is necessary to mention the question of uranium mining in Namibia. As Minister of Technology in the late 1960s, Tony Benn had signed a contract with RTZ and the UKAEA to secure Britain's uranium supply into the 1980s. Namibia, then as now, was occupied by South African troops, in defiance of the United Nations. Benn and the other Labour politicians involved have stated that they believed at the time that the contract involved RTZ-mined uranium from Canada, whereas in fact the uranium was eventually supplied from RTZ's Rossing mine in Namibia. Benn asserts that, as the minister involved, he was deliberately misled by RTZ, the UKAEA and senior civil servants at the Ministry of Technology.

Labour came to power in 1974 with a commitment from the 1973 Party conference to revoke the contract. The contract, however, was not revoked – despite a UN decree, in 1974, making it quite clear that such mining operations in Namibia should be regarded as 'illegal'. Callaghan declared a new approach to the Namibian question which recognized South Africa as the 'de facto administering authority', and the contract continued until the end of the Labour administration and beyond into the 1980s. Benn, as Energy Minister, was formally responsible for the receipt of enough Namibian uranium by BNFL to make up approximately 50 per cent of Britain's total needs.[10]

By the end of 1983, Benn himself had shifted ground considerably on the nuclear power issue – unlike either the shadow cabinet or the Labour Party conference. He now asserted that Windscale should be closed down, pending an independent inquiry; that British nuclear power stations had become 'bomb factories' for the USA; and that for Britain to 'act independently in pursuit of peace' it was necessary to adopt 'a non-nuclear defence policy and a non-nuclear energy policy'.[11]

Renewables   In practice, Labour in government supported just enough research and development into renewables to keep long-term options open – but no more. Even this came after criticism from 'official' quarters. Both the Flowers report on nuclear power, in 1976, and the Select Committee on Science and Technology, in 1977, criticized the level of expenditure on research into alternative or renewable sources of energy.[12] In 1976 only £3.7 million was spent on research and development into both renewable resources and conservation, while £146.3 million was spent on nuclear research and development.[13]

The government responded in 1978 with a £10 million research programme covering developments in solar, wind, wave and geothermal technologies. Nevertheless, the overall role ascribed to renewables remained minimal, except in the very long term. Benn's approach was that only when 'absolutely certain schemes' were developed, would alternative energy sources be allocated 'big money'.[14] This approach was not applied to nuclear power and it precluded the development of certain renewable technologies by starving the industry of funds at the outset.

Conservation   In comparison to renewables, the Labour government placed a much higher emphasis on conservation measures, and the level of expenditure in this field was also much higher. December 1974 saw the implementation of a 12-point energy conservation programme.[15] This involved heating and lighting restrictions on non-domestic buildings; higher thermal insulation standards for new houses; the reduction of the speed limit on motorways; loans for energy-saving programmes in industry; and the inauguration of the 'Save It' campaign. (In the event, the loans scheme to industry was unsuccessful – largely because the interest rates offered were little better than those in the commercial sector.) These measures were essentially a short-term response to the continuing 'oil crisis' which in 1974 took the form of rocketing oil prices and a massive national oil deficit of approaching £3½ thousand million. The immediate aim was to save £100 million in the coming year, and the measures should be seen as an emergency response rather than as part of any long-term plan.

From 1974-8 the government spent £8 million advertising conservation measures with the general aim of changing consumer habits through the provision of advice and information.[16] While trying to convince householders that energy conservation was 'economically rational', this approach failed to offer the individual sufficient financial incentive in the short term. 'Economic rationality' means that householders' decisions about what type of energy system to use tend to be determined by the relationship between cost and the amount of time they expect to remain in the same dwelling. Thus the best overall energy-effective systems will often not be chosen unless there are considerable short-term financial incentives from government. Attempts to change consumer energy use patterns by advertising alone are thus likely to have no more than a minor effect on levels of conservation and this was indeed the case with Labour's 'Save It' advertising campaign.

1978, however, saw a major commitment to conservation with the announcement of a £450 million programme over the next four years.[17] The programme included a £150 million insulation scheme for private and public housing, a further £150 million allocated to insulation and energy schemes in other public sector buildings, and a package of grant schemes, energy audits, advice, tax allowances, improvements in building regulations and demonstration projects of energy-saving technology for industry, commerce and agriculture. The scheme can be criticized for omitting any major conservation measures in transport and for the limited scope of the measures for industry. Although industry accounts for 35 per cent of total energy consumption, only £38 million was made available in this area – and most of that was for insulation schemes and demonstration projects. Little was done to implement major savings in the important field of industrial processes.[18] Whatever its potential, this scheme was cut short by the 1979 election and so it is difficult to evaluate what the possible effects might have been. Energy savings of up to £700 million a year (at 1978 prices) were estimated, however.[19] By 1981 the TUC Review of Energy Policy was to record that in less than two years the Tories had run down the project to the extent that it was 'in the process of collapse'.[20]

Finally, it is instructive to describe the important role in energy conservation given to the price mechanism by the Labour administration. From 1974, subsidies to the nationalized fuel industries began to be phased out, and together with rising raw material prices on the world market, this led to a phenomenal rise in energy prices to both domestic and industrial consumers. It has been estimated that energy savings of up to 6 per cent may have been made in 1975 through the price mechanism alone.[21] The impact of such a policy on the poor and those whose incomes do not rise quickly in response to inflation is significant – in winter higher energy prices lead directly to underheated homes.

Price-induced fuel poverty probably led to as much energy saving under Labour as all of the other energy conservation measures put together.

Energy policy 1974-9

Taken overall, Labour's energy policy from 1974-9 suffered from a tragically mistaken approach to economics and social change. It displayed the same, traditional overemphasis on nuclear power at the expense of other energy technologies shown by all British governments before or since. The one saving grace – a major programme of investment in conservation – came too late to take effect, and thus a considerable amount of the energy conservation achieved under Labour came quite simply by pricing the poor into underconsumption.

Perhaps the major virtue of the Labour government's energy programme was that it was so much better than the approach of the government that replaced it in 1979. Despite a general drift in the wrong direction, significant innovations took place which kept the way open for radical change in the future – namely the formation of the Energy Commission, the increased research and development on renewables, the extension of government control over oil resources and the new investments in the coal industry.

Energy policy and the 1983 election manifesto

The internal developments within the Labour Party from 1979-83 are not a direct concern here. Suffice it to say that the influence on party policy of the New Left, grouped broadly behind Tony Benn, petered out well before the 1983 election. The election manifesto,[22] despite its alleged radical content, was not essentially different in the fundamental area of economic policy from that of 1979 or 1974.

Perhaps most significant in the energy field was the growing prominence of a powerful anti-nuclear lobby within Labour's own ranks. By 1983 Labour had come out firmly against the PWR and there was an open split over nuclear policy as a whole between two rival party committees. While the Environmental Study Group advocated a strongly anti-nuclear and pro-renewables and conservation approach, the Energy Subcommittee continued to favour developments with the AGR and the fast breeder. It is discouraging that one of Neil Kinnock's first acts as party leader was to appoint an active opponent of the Environmental Study Group – Jack Cunningham – as environment spokesman. Both groups have now been disbanded with no immediate prospects of reforming.[23]

Overall, Labour went into the 1983 election with an energy policy based broadly on the practice of the 1974-9 administration but with several important and significant additions, namely opposition to the PWR, a commitment to CHP and a commitment to increased research and development on renewables. In conservation too, the manifesto promised an attempt to introduce an improved version of the 1978 programme. The manifesto also included a commitment to nuclear disarmament – a measure which, if implemented, would have necessitated a major restructuring of the economy and would have released resources from weapons production to other areas with subsequent far-reaching consequences for patterns of energy consumption.

This was clearly not a socialist energy policy. It was nevertheless more radical and more clearly presented than any other energy policy developed by Labour in the postwar period and if fully implemented would have had a marked and largely beneficial effect on the structure of energy use in Britain.

Local authority initiatives

In recent years some Labour local authorities have developed local energy plans. There are serious problems, however, caused by the limited amount of funding available. Many councils have drawn up wide-ranging schemes including CHP and extensive insulation and conservation measures. None have the available funds, however, to develop their own CHP schemes. The most extensive operational local energy plans have concentrated on energy advice and audits, insulation and draught-proofing projects, and on attempts to improve heating provision and energy use in council-owned buildings and council houses.

These are important initiatives. They raise the question of energy policy at a local level and, more importantly, do a little to improve heating provision to the poor. On the present scale, however, such schemes cannot make a major contribution to energy conservation or to bring about a major shift in patterns of energy use. In particular, insulation and draught-proofing projects which aim at the very poor are likely to alleviate fuel poverty without reducing energy consumption at all. Local authority energy initiatives are dealt with in detail in Chapter 8.

The trade union movement

Although the *TUC Review of Energy Policy* was not published until 1981, it nevertheless indicates the general direction of the

'official' TUC approach to energy for more than a decade from
1974. The review is a comprehensive document which mixes
defensive demands on the Tory government with some projections of future possibilities. Overall it advocates a move towards
energy self-sufficiency for the UK with nuclear power supplying
'a large proportion of energy requirements'.[24] One commentator
on the TUC's energy policy has observed that it sticks with existing options and asks for 'more of everything' – this in turn leads to
the acceptance of 'conservative estimates and arguments as to
future possibilities'.[25] Policies of individual unions, however,
have recently begun to differ considerably from the TUC's
approach, and an increasing number of unions are now adopting
anti-nuclear policies.

The review of energy policy, 1981
The 1979 Trade Union Congress passed a resolution calling for a
major review of energy policy, and in 1981 the Fuel and Power
Industries Committee (FPIC) duly published the required
report. Although calling for a fuller debate within the trade
union movement on future energy options, the motion had also
laid down the terms within which the report could operate – that
'for the foreseeable future . . . policy must depend crucially on
investment in this country's coal, nuclear and heavy engineering
industries'.[26]

The FPIC is made up of representatives from unions directly
involved in the energy field. Up to 1984 its long-standing chairman was Frank Chapple, the enthusiastically pro-nuclear secretary of the Electrical, Electronic, Telecommunications and
Plumbing Union (EETPU); the new chair is Chapple's successor
at the EETPU, Eric Hammond. The relationship between the
different unions and the energy industry as a whole is a complex
one. Of the major unions only the National Union of Mineworkers (NUM) has all of its members directly involved in the industry. For the others, union membership cuts across different areas
of the energy sector, and for each union a different proportion of
the total membership is involved in energy. The General and
Municipal Workers Union (GMWU), the Transport and General Workers Union (TGWU) and the Amalgamated Union of

Engineering Workers (AUEW) all have a large number of members spread across different sections of the industry, but for each union the total in energy represents only a small proportion of their membership. The white collar unions NALGO (National and Local Government Officers Association) and ASTMS (Association of Scientific, Technical and Managerial Staffs) are in a similar position, although fewer workers are involved. The civil services unions also have a small number of members in the nuclear industry and at the Department of Energy. The situation is different for the EETPU where, while the proportion of members in energy remains low, they are concentrated in one sector – electricity supply. Finally, there is the Engineers and Managers Association (EMA) which incorporates the old Electrical Power Engineers Association (EPEA) and which is headed by Chapple's major pro-nuclear ally, John Lyons. EMA members are primarily involved in electricity supply.[27]

One of the results of this wide spread of representation is that the FPIC attempts to protect the interests of all its members at once, and consequently long-term energy policy, tends to reflect the short-term goal of maintaining existing levels and patterns of employment. Another significant fact about the FPIC is that with the exception of the NUM, all the major unions on the committee have members in the nuclear industry. This means that there has been little direct opposition to the pro-nuclear stance of Chapple and Lyons, and leads to the committee's heavy emphasis on nuclear power. Since 1980 the NUM has been opposed to any further nuclear developments, recognizing among other factors that nuclear power was being developed as a direct means of undermining the strength of their union.

On international issues the document is remarkably narrow in outlook. Predictions of a major international energy crisis by the year 2000 are accepted uncritically. No mention is made of the social and technological developments which might deflect the predicted threefold increase in world energy demand. The conclusion drawn is that faced with such an international crisis, Britain had better be self-sufficient in energy supply. The only practical solutions offered at international level are for a UK programme of energy technology aid to the Third World – which would be laudable, but for the stated commitment to nuclear power – and for the establishment of a powerful international energy planning authority (within which, presumably, the TUC's voice would be minimal).

No mention is made of the exploitative activities of the multinationals in the energy field, nor of measures to curb the operations of those that are British-based. Uranium mining is considered only in terms of the problems of guaranteeing supply and not – even in relation to Namibia – in terms of international solidarity between workers and trade unions in the energy field.

In its forecasts the document estimates a wider possible range of total energy demand by the year 2000 than the Department of Energy's 1979 figures. Where the Department of Energy predicted demand ranging from 445 to 510 mtce per annum, the TUC predicts a range from 400 to 550 mtce.[28] The higher figure is reached by using an economic growth estimate of 3 per cent per annum for each year up to the year 2000. A Friends of the Earth comment on the Department of Energy figures stated that 'they assume that economic growth will be higher within the next two decades than it has been since the war, but do not attempt to justify this assumption. Its assumed rate of economic growth appears to be higher than that of any other forecasting body in this country',[29] though not, evidently, higher than the TUC's.

On the basis of this higher estimate, and linked to the assumed need for energy self-sufficiency, the TUC argues for a major production programme in the power plant industry. In the light of the small number of domestic orders in recent years (due to the excess generating capacity of the CEGB and SSEB) this programme is explicitly linked to the survival of the industry itself and to the immediate job prospects of its members. The TUC proposes a minimum annual construction programme of two gigawatts per annum until the year 2000 (this is the equivalent of three or four conventional power stations of average size or about one and three-quarter Sizewell PWRs per year). The policy reserves judgement on the PWR but proposes the immediate ordering of a new AGR station and asserts its support for a 'continuing programme of nuclear power station construction based on thermal reactors designed and built in the UK – along with the development of fast reactor technology'.[30]

The document singles out for criticism the IIED's low-energy strategy (see Chapter 6) which argues that with a wider-ranging energy conservation programme the UK could have 50 years of relatively high growth and end up using less energy than it does today.[31] One implication of this is that the TUC's planned expansion of the electricity supply industry would become unnecessary. The IIED strategy is refuted on the basis that it relies on unproven technology – ironic in the light of the TUC's commitment to the fast reactor.

On the positive side the document calls for an expanded version of Labour's 1978 conservation programme, backed by £1 billion of government spending drawn from increasing the North Sea oil revenues to the exchequer. Significant additions to the 1978 programme include a commitment to CHP, improved building regulations, greater emphasis on domestic insulation, the establishment of local energy centres and finally the creation of an energy conservation agency aimed at increasing the role of conservation measures in the formation and implementation of energy policy. Additional proposals include an allocation of between £30 and £50 million per annum for research and development on renewables and a commitment to energy savings in transport – through the maintenance of a modern and efficient public transport system and through providing funds for investment into more energy efficient vehicles.[32]

With regard to renewables, however, the TUC endorses the 'conservative estimate of their potential made by the Department of Energy in 1979 (Energy Paper 39)', concluding that they would make little contribution to energy provision by the year 2000.[33] The 1978 Green Paper, which similarly omits renewables from its scenario for the year 2000 is explicitly referred to as a 'landmark' in energy policy.[34]

On coal, oil and gas the document carries a detailed critique of Tory policy from 1979 on. In oil and gas, the argument is essentially against the rapid depletion of resources, against privatization, and for a return to the 1979 state of the industry. In coal, the 1980 Coal Industry Act is criticized for forcing operation according to financial limits, rather than production targets.[35] The 1974 Plan for Coal is recognized as the basis from which the industry should continue to operate and continue to expand.

Along with the Labour Party, the TUC now recognizes CHP as a viable development in energy policy based on proven and readily available technology. The promise of a major programme of public works in this area, with the subsequent creation of both jobs and of cheap, efficient heating make CHP an important part of the TUC's energy strategy.

Essentially, the 1981 TUC Review of Energy Policy calls for a return to the approach to energy adopted by Labour from 1974-9 with the addition of greater emphasis on conservation measures *and* greater emphasis on the development of nuclear power. The net result of this, if implemented, even with high economic growth, would undoubtedly be a gross excess of electricity generating capacity with subsequent higher costs to the consumer for maintaining it. It is a document which would return the TUC to a high level of involvement and recognition in national planning, would preserve the 1974-9 status quo in the energy industry, and would guarantee medium-term job security for those energy workers in unions represented on the FPIC. As such, the whole document depends on a strategy for conventional economic growth through government spending. At best it might avoid disruptive structural changes in the economy until after the year 2000. At worst it relies on policies which would place the TUC in the position of jointly managing, along with a Labour government, an economy which would be incapable of sustained growth or of incorporating any major social or economic reforms.

New directions on energy?
Motions passed at recent TUC conferences have not altered the general direction of policy on energy. There is considerable tension within the TUC over the nuclear power issue with the result that energy motions passed at conference tend to be those that sit on the fence, reflecting neither the total opposition of the NUM and others, nor the high enthusiasm of the EETPU. At the 1983 conference a motion of this nature was proposed calling for

balanced development of energy resources and a programme of energy conservation . . . research and develpment of alternative energy sources, energy technology aid for developing countries, recognition of the key role of coal, continuation of the nuclear programme but with public debate on safety, and a steady home ordering programme so that the power plant industry could plan ahead.[36]

The motion was passed by a show of hands. The 1983 conference also saw a major debate over the PWR in which a motion proposing total opposition and giving support to possible AGR developments (moved by NACODS, the small mining union of pit deputies) was manoeuvred aside by an amendment from John Lyons which made opposition contingent on the conclusions of the Sizewell Inquiry. This amendment was carried by a narrow majority.[37] At the 1984 conference the tensions within the TUC around energy policy and general strategy came into the open with Eric Hammond making the leading speech in opposition to the miners' strike. Although the strike dominated the conference, no new developments were made in energy policy. In 1985, the TUC's established PWR policy was reaffirmed, together with a call for the expansion of the coal industry. The crucial question, coal *or* nuclear power was fudged once more.

While the pro-nuclear lobby has successfully maintained its control over TUC energy policy during the last decade, many individual unions have adopted a very different stance. In 1978 it was possible to write that 'the vast majority of British trade unions are at present firmly committed to nuclear power',[38] by 1982 ten unions at national level were officially anti-nuclear, including the NUM, NUPE, UCATT, USDAW and COHSE. The TGWU also became an anti-nuclear union in 1985. More generally, by the 1980 conference only those unions with members directly involved in the industry overtly supported nuclear power. There has been a trend for unions outside the nuclear field to develop policies in energy emphasizing conservation and the importance of research and development into renewable and alternative energy sources.[39] It is significant also that not all unions have accepted the high demand estimates of the Department of Energy and the TUC. The GMWU, for example, estimate that the maximum energy demand by the year 2000 is likely to be only 400 mtce.[40] In addition, many unions which are not explicitly anti-nuclear are now opposed to the PWR (e.g. GMWU, NALGO) and favour either a freeze on further nuclear developments or a replacement-only policy, often subject to some form of public review of the industry or to the introduction of higher safety standards.

It would be quite wrong to attribute these developments specifically to the work of particular pressure groups and anti-nuclear organizations – the problems with the AGR programme and the inaccuracy of CEGB and Department of Energy demand forecasting in the past can stand on their own as good reasons for reassessing one's support for a nuclear energy policy. Nevertheless, the orientation towards trade unions of both the Socialist Environment and Resources Association (SERA) and, until recently, the Anti-Nuclear Campaign (ANC) must be taken into account, as must the impact of other pressure groups – notably Greenpeace and Friends of the Earth – on public opinion, and thus in turn on the views of individual trade unionists. The ease with which Greenpeace, in December 1983, raised over £30,000 to pay a fine imposed for action taken at Windscale, and the extent of the public response at Billingham and Elstow to proposals to set up nuclear waste dumps in the vicinity, indicates how widespread informed opinion has become. It would be strange if the trade union movement failed to reflect this trend.

Conclusions

The official Labour and TUC approach to energy and economics has changed little over the last decade. Policy still reflects the 1960s Keynsian consensus aiming at a shift towards equality through economic growth without any major redistribution of income or power and without major structural change.

Meanwhile, unions in the energy sector have suffered from similar problems to unions in other sectors of the economy. A combination of the effects of the world recession, of increasing automation, of the development of new high technology industries, and of a concerted attack on trade union organization both at national level and in the workplace has led to a major restructuring of the British economy.

Unemployment has risen to around the 4 million mark and the number of workers employed in the manufacturing industry, in particular, has fallen considerably. The British economy appears to be in the throes of a long-term shift away from the traditional centres of industry in the engineering and metal trades. Where unions, workplaces, communities and local authorities have resisted this process they have not been given the full support of the Labour and TUC leadership. Both appear to look back towards the fading glory of a social contract that failed, rather than to face the reality in which they now operate. The bargaining power of the movement's traditional giants in the mining and manufacturing industries has declined as the industries themselves have been decimated by Thatcher's enforced recession. At the same time there is little sign of a developing militant trade unionism in any new industries.

Taken as a whole, all of these factors imply a considerable reduction in the likelihood of workers bringing about major shifts in their favour either in material terms or in terms of wider policy changes. Progress now demands a political trade unionism – a merging of new political strategies with a renewed commitment to basic trade union recruitment and education.

Future perspectives for energy policy therefore depend on two main factors: firstly, environmentalist, anti-nuclear and socialist groups should continue to feed radical proposals on energy into official Labour movement channels – although we are nearing the limit to the number of radical additions that can be made without altering the whole direction of policy. This leads on to the second factor – the wider prospects for the movement as a whole. Whatever else the regeneration of a socialist tradition involves, it must include the rebuilding of an effective trade unionism in the workplace in both established industries and those in creation.

It is with this in mind that a socialist approach to energy must be framed. Critiques of the Labour and TUC programme should be linked into energy-related struggles in the workplace and the community. If industry and society are to be reconstructed in the interests of the working class, then energy issues are going to be at the centre of socialist strategies and struggles for years to come.

In 1985, the Labour Party Conference voted for a motion calling for a 'halt to the nuclear power programme and a phasing out of all existing plants'. The motion narrowly missed achieving the two-thirds majority necessary to guarantee a place in the manifesto for the next general election. This leaves room for conjecture as to the energy policy of a future Labour government but clearly it strengthens the position of those who are pushing for radical change.

5. Tory energy strategy

Until the early 1970s, there was a broad consensus on the general direction of British energy policy. The rundown of coal, the slow build-up of nuclear power and the acceptance of dependency on imported oil proceeded under both Labour and Tory governments. In the previous chapter, it was argued that the 1974-9 Labour government started in modest ways to break with this consensus and to subject energy policy and energy planning to a more open process of debate and to a more clearly defined set of priorities. The Tories, in office since 1979, completed the rupture with the previous consensus. At the same time, however, they have taken matters in an altogether different direction.

The Tories are the party of business, of private enterprise. They make no secret of it, they receive their funding from private companies and they make a virtue of subjecting public bodies to 'businesslike' profit-oriented priorities. It would be too crude, however, to analyse Tory policies as if they were a simple and direct reflection of the interests of private enterprise: for one thing different companies have different interests and benefit in different ways from government spending and taxation policies. The avowed aim of the Tory Party under Thatcher's leadership is to create an environment in which private enterprise can thrive, and clearly this means dealing with certain obstacles, such as a powerful and independent trade union movement. Having said that, however, many problems and contradictions remain. These contradictions are frequently expressed by arguments within the Tory Party between a radical ideological faction, believing in 'free market' principles as an item of faith and enjoying the patronage of Thatcher herself, and a more traditional pragmatic faction, seeking to rebuild the Tories as the party of 'One Nation', enjoying broad cross-class support.

The actions of the Thatcher government on the energy front are best understood when seen in this context. Tory energy strategy is part of the overall programme for profitable private enterprise, but at the same time it reflects the struggles within the party over the best means to this end. In fact energy policy is highly instructive in revealing the internal logic and the incoherence of the Tory programme as a whole.

The economic context

Much has been written in recent years on the 'deindustrialization' of the British economy. This term is misleading. The UK economy is certainly undergoing a significant shift away from manufacturing and primary industries and towards the service sector: this is a long-term trend which has accelerated in recent years. However, it is not 'deindustrializing' in some absolute sense, but is rather undergoing a process of industrial restructuring, away from an old set of core industries (such as textiles, heavy engineering and motors) and towards a new set (electrical engineering, electronics and oil). At the same time, Britain remains an attractive site for foreign industrial investment, from the USA above all, but also from Western Europe and increasingly from Japan. None of this is intended to deny the reality of Britain's long-term economic crisis – but it is important to have a clear view of the form of that crisis and to appreciate that Britain will remain a significant industrial country for the foreseeable future.

Energy requirements must be linked to these broad trends. From the point of view of the Tory Party, concerned as it is to encourage the activities of British and foreign companies within the UK, it is essential that there should be a secure and flexible electricity supply system as part of the necessary infrastructure for economic activity. What this means above all, for reasons discussed at length later (see Chapter 7), is a secure electricity supply system. The political and technical security of the electricity supply network is therefore one essential component of Tory energy strategy.

The second major component centres on oil. North Sea oil in

the 1980s is *the* key industrial sector in the national economy, generating profits, contributing to an otherwise disastrous balance of payments and underwriting the finances of the state. The development of the North Sea's energy resources is therefore of significance not only for energy policy but for the economy as a whole.

Tory energy strategy is not something which has been spelled out in speeches or laid down in documents. On the contrary, the Tory Party today is hostile to anything which smacks of 'planning', and former Energy Secretary Lawson used to take delight in publicly denying that the government even had an 'energy policy'.[1] Nevertheless, a study of events since the 1970s reveals that a coherent strategy does exist and is being implemented.

Restructuring electricity

The miners' strikes of the early 1970s made a profound impression on both Tory politicians and civil servants. In their eyes, the country's electricity supply system was dangerously dependent upon a single fuel, coal, and the supply of coal was dangerously vulnerable to industrial action by two or three key trade unions. Within the state bureaucracy, the central institution of the Treasury became convinced that nuclear power offered the best prospects as a strategic alternative to coal. When Treasury men subsequently pursued their careers as mandarins in other departments, they carried the nuclear faith with them, exemplified by Sir Jack Rampton, who moved to the Department of Energy, and Sir Kenneth Berrill, who went to the Central Policy Review Staff.[2]

The Tory Party meanwhile concentrated on the most immediate aspects of the problem – defeating the National Union of Mineworkers (NUM). In May 1978, the existence of a Tory policy document came to light, in which a series of measures were proposed for a future confrontation with the miners. These included:

☐ Building up coal-stocks, especially at power stations;
☐ Making contingency plans for the import of coal;

☐ Encouraging hauliers to recruit non-union drivers;
☐ Introducing dual oil-and-coal firing at power stations;
☐ Cutting off state benefits to strikers and making the union finance them;
☐ Establishing a large, mobile police squad to deal with pickets.[3]

The carefully calculated approach of the Tories has continued to be evident. In 1981 the government found itself in dispute with the NUM over pit closures – and it backed down. In the words of David Howell, Energy Minister at the time, the government was 'not ready' to confront the miners. By 1984, however, it *was* ready. Coal stocks were at record levels; large oil-fired power stations, ordered in the 1960s and early 1970s, provided a major back-up to coal-fired capacity; nuclear capacity was greater than ever before; and police forces were becoming experienced at organizing large national operations against the labour movement. In March 1984, the government's new NCB Chairman, MacGregor, announced a crash programme of pit closures and reduced production, with the clear intention of provoking the NUM to strike.

The Tories' hostility to the NUM, and to effective trade unionism in general, is intimately connected with their enthusiasm for nuclear power. In November 1979, six months after the Tories took office, leaked Cabinet minutes revealed the prevailing thinking on electricity supply: 'a nuclear programme would have the advantage of removing a substantial portion of electricity production from the dangers of industrial action by coal miners or transport workers'. This represented the coalescence of the Treasury's concerns (with their strategic emphasis on the merits of nuclear power), and the Tory Party report, (with its tactical stress on defeating the miners).

The advantages of nuclear power, for the Tory Party and for private enterprise, are many. First, nuclear technology is highly complex and expensive, demanding massive initial investment, thus lending itself to monopolization by a few large companies. As was made clear earlier (see Chapter 2), UK reactor building capacity has been largely structured since the early 1970s around GEC, while uranium supply is dominated by RTZ. An expanded nuclear programme could only be to the benefit of these and other leading British companies, and this in itself, in Tory eyes, could only be of benefit to Britain.

Second, nuclear power promises relative security from indust-rial action by workers. As a highly capital-intensive undertaking, it employs comparatively few workers for billions of pounds invested. This workforce is, furthermore, highly differentiated and fragmented, and many of its key members are skilled white-collar or technical workers. While highly unionized, the nuclear industry therefore lends itself to a rightwing, elitist and frag-mented trade union structure. It presents a difficult environment in which to create a sense of common shared interests within the workforce. It lends itself, instead, to atomization and the erec-tion of hierarchies. The peculiar and extreme hazards associated with nuclear activities only add to these problems. They provide a standing justification for management to deny information to workers or the public in the name of 'public safety' and 'security'.

Third, there is the link between nuclear power and nuclear weapons. It would be far too crude to suggest that the Tories want to build nuclear power stations simply to produce plutonium for nuclear bombs. However, for a government which is committed to a major programme of nuclear rearmament, it is technically and industrially logical for a parallel expansion of the 'civil' nuclear programme also to take place. Many of the facilities used by the nuclear power programme – enrichment plant, reprocessing works, reactors themselves – are also used by the nuclear weapons programme. The expansion of such facilities for 'peaceful' nuclear power thus has an added justifica-tion in that it also provides a readily available infrastructure for an expanded nuclear arsenal. In the course of the Windscale Inquiry of 1977 and the Sizewell Inquiry of 1983-5, it has become clear that there is no material or technical dividing line between the 'civil' and 'military' programmes. An expanded nuclear power programme may well have an additional military rationale.

Given all these factors, it is hardly surprising that the govern-ment is committed to the expansion of nuclear power, on the basis of an imported reactor design and imported uranium, at the expense of domestically mined coal. In its evidence to the Sizewell Inquiry, the Department of Energy projected that power stations would at most be burning only three-quarters as much coal in 2010 as in 1980. At worst, they might be burning less than half. Nuclear power output would meanwhile have risen at least fourfold, and perhaps tenfold.[4]

An added twist is given to the struggle between nuclear power and coal by the construction of a cross-channel link between the British and French electricity grids. In effect, this allows the UK to import surplus French electricity now being generated by that country's massive, and massively expensive, nuclear power programme. Coal is thus being undermined not only by British but also by French nuclear power.

However, the electricity supply system does not need to receive its inputs exclusively from coal and nuclear power. Oil-fired power stations are still significant. They provided about 7 per cent of electricity supplied in 1981-2,[5] and very much more during the 1984-5 miners' strike. In fact, the CEGB's main response to the strike was to switch to oil-fired electricity on a massive scale and at enormous cost. There are also a range of potential energy sources which could contribute to electricity needs, given the resources for research and development, and pilot schemes. These sources, the renewables, are discussed at length above, (see p.51). However, the Tory government has instituted major funding cuts for nearly all the renewables, with wind power alone still enjoying some muted recognition. Nuclear power continues to receive the lion's share of energy research and development, as it has done for years past. Over the years 1975 to 1981, cumulative government research and development expenditure on *all* the renewables was only one-fifteenth of the amount spent on the fast reactor *alone*, and the fast reactor is only one line of nuclear research.[6] Renewable funds were further cut back in 1982, following a government review.

From the point of view of the Tory Party, and of large-scale private enterprise, renewable sources of energy are a problem. They require no fuel and they potentially lend themselves to a locally based, decentralized energy structure. Both of these factors reduce their potential as generators of profit – and private companies' investment decisions are made in order to realize a profit, not to produce something which may be socially useful. Much of the attraction of the energy sector, as far as private capital is concerned, lies in the long-term contracts for fuel supply and in the provision of complex and centralized technologies which require long-term servicing and maintenance. With renewables many of these profitable activities are reduced or cut out. This is not to deny that certain private companies are able to make a modest profit from renewable energy technologies, but the scale of their activity, compared to the scale of activity in such mainstream areas as oil, gas, coal and nuclear power, is tiny. The existence of certain marginal or minority markets for the renewables – such as small island communities – should not be allowed to obscure the fact that capital doesn't like them.

Another sign of the restructuring of electricity supply was the Tory Energy Act of 1983. This allows private companies to generate electricity and sell it to the electricity boards at controlled prices. It also gives these companies the right to buy supplies from the boards. In theory, the Act opens up a new range of possibilities for the electricity supply industry – from significant investment by private capital to municipal combined heat and power/district heating schemes. In practice, these opportunities were not taken up in the first two years of the Act's operation.

However, more radical privatization proposals for the industry are also on the agenda, these may grant to private interests not merely the right to set up their own new power stations, but the far more tempting prospect of cashing in on the CEGB 's existing operations, built up over 50 years with public money. One option is to sell off all or part of the CEGB, while retaining it as a single body; another is to establish competing regional supply companies, based on the existing area boards; and a third is to privatize coal-mines and power stations together, thus benefiting from 'economies of integration'.[7] Powerful figures in the industry are in favour of some form of privatization. The chairman of the Electricity Council, for instance, wants to be allowed to operate as 'a Companies Act company'.[8]

To sum up, the restructuring of the electricity supply system consists of a steady rundown of coal, a steady build-up of nuclear power, and a studied disregard for the potential of the renewables. In all of these areas, technical, economic and political considerations overlap to the point where they cannot be distinguished.

North Sea oil

The North Sea has been a blessing to the Tories. It has made the UK almost unique among advanced capitalist countries in removing the need for net oil imports, thus saving billions of pounds each year. It has provided a whole new growth sector in the economy, generating profits, downstream activity and jobs. Its earnings have disguised the full extent of manufacturing industrial decline and transformed the balance of payments. Finally, royalties and tax income have made a major contribution to the state's finances, allowing the Tories to maintain spending while avoiding tax increases or extra borrowing.

These issues need spelling out for their significance to be appreciated. In the economy at large, the oil industry provides significant but not extensive employment: 20,000 jobs, plus a further 100,000 onshore in support and auxiliary services.[9] Its impact on investment patterns has been much more dramatic: between 1973 and 1983, £30 billion was invested in the North Sea,[10] and from 1975 to 1981 it accounted for 42 per cent of all manufacturing industry fixed investment in the UK.[11]

The impact of oil revenues on the state's finances were spelled out by Energy Minister Walker in 1983, when he stated that the loss of these revenues would increase income tax by one-third and raise interest rates through an increase in public borrowing.[12] The Tories have been exceptionally fortunate in that this enormous subsidy to state finances has become available precisely during their term of office. In 1979, oil revenues accounted for less than 1 per cent of government tax income, but by 1983 it had risen to 14 per cent.[13]

Since North Sea oil plays this crucial role of effectively subsidizing the Tories' whole economic programme, their oil policy centres on the single priority of maximizing output. However, high oil production cannot be taken for granted: it can only occur within a satisfactory market and fiscal environment which encourages exploration and drilling to locate further reserves. By 1982 it was clear that many of the biggest, earliest and most easily exploited oilfields were past their peak. A new round of government approvals for new projects therefore went through, leading to a 'second boom' in exploration and drilling by the end of 1983. Exploration hit record levels in 1983, and again in 1984,[14] not only offshire but also onshore especially in the south of England.

The second wave of expansion has been engineered for two reasons. Firstly, it will in itself launch a new round of investment in the North Sea, sustaining it in its role as the nation's new core industry. It has been estimated that £30-£60 billion may be invested in the North Sea over the next 15 years.[15] Furthermore, this 'second boom' sets the scene for the Tories to continue with their economic policies, underwritten by the North Sea oil earnings, potentially into the 1990s. Tax revenues are expected to peak in 1985-6, but may still be significant in the years immediately following.

An expansionist, high-production policy in the North Sea, exploiting the oil's potential as a marketable commodity and ignoring its value as an energy resource for the future, is therefore at the heart of Tory energy strategy and indeed at the heart of Tory economic strategy. However, the price paid by the economy as a whole is very high. First, the rapid development of North Sea oil has actually accelerated the decline of other industrial sectors. Since oil is such a sought-after commodity, the existence of British oil conferred new status upon the pound sterling in the early 1980s giving it a high value in foreign exchange markets, making it difficult for other British manufacturers to export their goods and forcing many to reduce capacity by laying off workers or closing down altogether.

Second, rapid development has involved large-scale involvement of foreign capital in the North Sea, especially by the US oil companies. In 1980, foreign companies accounted for 56 per cent of North Sea oil output, and US companies alone for 39 per cent.[16] Of the five biggest-producing oilfields in the North Sea to the end of 1982, Piper was entirely owned by US and Canadian companies; Beryl, 90 per cent owned by US companies; Brent,

50 per cent owned by a US company; and Ninian, 37 per cent owned by US and Canadian companies.[17] Only BP's 96 per cent holding in the Forties field breaks the pattern. This US penetration of the North Sea is no accident – it is the inevitable consequence of a policy of rapid production which implies reliance on those companies already dominant in the industry.

Problems and contradictions

The contradiction at the heart of the Tory government's oil policy was identified in Chapter 2. Oil policy is intended to underwrite an ideologically founded economic strategy, but it can only do so by undermining those same ideological principles. In the same way, other aspects of Tory energy strategy and economic strategy more broadly, face serious problems and inconsistencies.

For instance, there is the commitment to privatization of public energy assets as part of the wider privatization programme, with its populist rhetoric of handing state corporations 'back to the people'. In November 1982, BNOC was split into two parts: the production arm was renamed Britoil, and a 51 per cent holding was floated on the stock exchange, complete with its North Sea reserves. Meanwhile the marketing operation was retained as a sadly reduced BNOC in state ownership. Britoil's initial flotation was a flop, but by December 1983 82 per cent of the private shares were held by just 383 large institutional investors.[18] The next privatization measure was in June 1984, when the British Gas Corporation's (BGC's) North Sea oil holdings were converted into a private company, Enterprise Oil, and sold off. This time the government was embarrassed not by the market's lack of interest, but rather by the excessive interest shown by one multinational company, RTZ. It attempted a virtual takeover of Enterprise, was blocked by the government, but has subsequently built up its holding through share dealing.[19] In the first half of 1985 the government made several more announcements along similar lines: the complete abolition of BNOC; the privatization of its remaining 49 per cent stake in Britoil; and the privatization of the BGC at an estimated price of £8 billion. Next in line may be selective privatization of profitable super-pits, alongside continuing closure of those coal-mines deemed to be 'uneconomic'.

However, in all this there is a very clear gap between rhetoric and reality. Privatization in reality means handing over public assets to large financial institutions and multinational companies. It does not end monopoly, but merely transfers it into different hands. Cabinet discussions on the possible privatization of the BGC and CEGB have pretended to tackle this issue by proposing a radical subdivision of these bodies, so that existing area or regional boards would be transformed into competing private companies.[20] The very nature of electricity and gas supply lends itself to monopolization, however, and in the event the BGC is indeed to be sold off as a single body. And the very nature of the stock market means that share-trading after the initial sale will transfer from small shareholders to large institutions.

Belief in the superiority of private enterprise is a key element in Tory philosophy, but in a sector as fundamental as the energy sector it runs up against problems. On the one hand, privatization ought to mean more efficiently run energy industries, according to Tory theory. On the other hand, privatization actually places invaluable assets in the hands of large, capitalist companies and confers upon these companies the potential to dictate national energy policy in their own interests. RTZ is a good example: its attempt to gain a large stake in Enterprise Oil would have given it an unacceptably powerful position in the North Sea, so the government, for all its non-interventionist rhetoric, had to step in to block it. There must at some point be a conflict between the Tories' intention to provide a secure, flexible energy infrastructure, in order to serve private capital in general, and their intention to privatize energy supply, which leads to the growing domination of energy industries by particular private companies. In effect, by proceeding with privatization, the Tory government is renouncing its own ability to act in the interests of private enterprise as a whole.

As a result, reservations about privatization and about the whole direction of Tory energy strategy are not confined to the labour movement or the Left. They are deeply rooted in the state machinery itself. The state is not, of course, a neutral instrument, placing itself willingly at the service of whichever party is in power; the institutions and relations which constitute the state are politically loaded, reflecting and legitimizing vested interests.[21] In the past, civil servants and state functionaries have worked more easily with a Tory government than with any other, because the Tories have been perceived as the party of tradition, stability and vested interest. However, when a *radical* Tory government comes to office, such as the present one, seeking to redefine the nature of public enterprise and to redefine the boundary between public and private sectors, then problems appear. Within the public energy corporations, the result has been a series of battles, pitting radical elements in the government which are seeking to impose commercial criteria upon the corporations, against technocrats and engineers within corporations, whose loyalty is to their industries and to a traditional conception of 'public service'.

The government's strategy (especially when Lawson was at the Department of Energy) has been to appoint its own political supporters as chairmen of energy corporations and to back them up by creating new part-time board places which can also be filled by sympathizers from private industry, banking and the professions. In this way outside 'experts', for whom profitability is the crucial issue, can outvote the engineers and administrators who have spent a lifetime in the industries. The National Coal Board is a classic example: government appointee Ian MacGregor (a banker) can count on the regular support of the six part-time members who have a majority on the board and who are all personally known to him.[22] This led to regular rows inside the NCB during the 1984-5 miners' strike, when the board adopted a highly provocative stance completely at odds with the traditions of many of its own long-standing officials, which led in some cases to resignations and dismissals.[23] However, the NCB is not unique: most of the nationalized industries have a majority of outside part-timers on their boards. This is true of BNOC, the Electricity Council, the North of Scotland Hydro Electricity Board, the South of Scotland Electricity Board and the United Kingdom Atomic Energy Authority.[24]

The placing of board members is only one part of the wider strategy which is to subordinate public energy policy to commercial priorities, and specifically to the priorities of the bankers. Ian MacGregor, at the NCB, is a banker from the US end of the merchant bank Lazards. Philip Shelbourne, Chairman, first of BNOC, and then of Britoil, is a banker from the merchant bank Samuel Montagu. These merchant banks – the financial elite of the City who act as advisers on investment policy, company flotations, mergers, takeovers and the whole complex business of corporate life – are deeply involved in the Tory government's energy strategy. Leading merchant bank Kleinwort Benson has long been associated with the nuclear industry , and specifically with attempts by the US multinational Westinghouse, to build its PWR in Britain.[25] The privatization of the nuclear materials company, Amersham International, was handled by merchant banks N.M. Rothschild and Morgan Grenfell. Britoil was handled by Rothschild and Warburg. Enterprise Oil was handled by Kleinwort Benson. The merchant banks are exercising a growing influence over nationalized energy industries and over the process whereby some of these are privatized.

The major exception to this trend, the main point of technocratic resistance to the influx of bankers, has been in the British Gas Corporation (BGC). Its Chairman, Sir Denis Rooke, is the public sector's longest-serving chairman, an engineer and chemist who has been in the industry since 1949. He has publicly rowed with Lawson over energy policy, and openly states, 'I don't believe in bringing in merchant bankers to run things.'[26] Rooke is no socialist, and claims to be neutral in his attitude towards the privatization of the BGC so long as the corporation retains its integrity and is allowed to operate within an adequate regulatory framework. But he is a symbol of the deep antipathy to Thatcherism among engineers and scientists whose primary commitment is to the real economy, to material production, and not to the logic of short-term profit and loss.

These conflicts do not merely pit radicalism in the government against certain layers of public officials: they are also evident within the Tory Party, and even within the Cabinet. Once again energy policy provides the most acute illustration in that the

Energy Department has been headed successively by the Cabinet's most convinced monetarist – Lawson – and by its leading pragmatist – Walker.

Energy conservation is an area in which these different approaches have emerged quite clearly. Under Lawson's guidance, the approach to energy conservation was unapologetically ideological: 'the explicit role of market prices in determining energy demand removes the need for a separate allowance for energy conservation'.[27] Walker, on the other hand, has made energy conservation his public priority. He has called for 20 per cent energy savings, worth £7 billion,[28] and set up an Energy Efficiency Office in 1983. In practice, the Walker approach consists of an attempt to persuade businessmen that energy efficiency is in their own best commercial interests, and while he has applied himself to this task, the money available to help ordinary people carry out basic domestic insulation has been steadily cut back as a result of central government restrictions on local government spending. Nevertheless, the difference in emphasis between Lawson and Walker is evident.

These differences came to a head in late 1983 when the two ministers clashed publicly over gas and electricity price rises. The interesting point about the row was that the Tory tabloid press – that part of the press which most effectively shapes and reflects the government's mass support in the country – unanimously supported Walker in his resistance to Lawson's price rises.[30] These bickerings are of interest not because of the personalities involved but because of the deeper issues to which they point. They demonstrate that the single-minded pursuit of radical Tory policies, in the energy field as in many others, is quite capable of generating widespread disaffection within the Tories' own base of electoral support.

To sum up, Tory energy strategy is full of contradictions even in its own terms. The fundamental aim, which is shared by all factions within the Tory Party, is to provide an energy infrastructure suitable for the needs of private enterprise, and this involves a restructuring of the energy supply system away from coal and towards nuclear power, and the continued rapid development of North Sea oil. It also implies the injection of commercial criteria, the dominance of market forces, the breaking up of monopolies and, in some cases, privatization of public energy assets. In modern conditions, however, the real effect of this strategy is to hand over control of energy supply to large multinational corporations. It reduces the power of any future British government, including a Tory government, to carry out its economic and social policies effectively at a national level. It mortgages energy resources and future energy options to large-scale private companies whose loyalty is not to any national economy but to their own global profit margins. In other words, there is a profound contradiction between the Tories' character as the party of private enterprise, and their character as the party of patriotism and the national interest.

It is this same contradiction which generates opposition among engineers and scientists in the energy industries. They may not be fundamentally hostile to the market economy, but they realize that any modern economy must be underpinned by a complex technical infrastructure, and they regard it as against the national interest to risk damaging that infrastructure by subjecting it to arbitrary commercial criteria. The imposition of market forces can be deeply offensive to engineers and technicians motivated by a sense of professionalism and of public service. Once again, the abstract commitment to free enterprise runs up against the concrete reality of the existing national economy.

Ultimately these contradictions may seriously erode the Tories' electoral base. The Tory tabloids' support for Walker against Lawson over energy prices indicates that Tory voters may not endorse the extension of 'market forces' into an area as fundamental as energy supply.

There is no guarantee that these contradictions must be realized. It is possible that the government will continue to gloss over the problems and defeat its outright opponents, thus holding its problems at bay. However, for those of us who are seeking to change the direction of energy policy and to prioritize social and environmental responsibility rather than commercial advantage, it is necessary to be aware of the contradictions of the Tories' strategy and to be prepared to exploit them.

6. Alternative energy forecasts and Green politics in the UK

Labour movement policy has tended to start from a set of conventional assumptions about the self-evident desirability of capitalist economic growth and the self-evident desirability of rising energy consumption (see Chapter 4). These are the principles which underpinned the all-party consensus on energy policy in the 1950s, 1960s and early 1970s. Experience over the past decade has shown just how fragile these assumptions are. It is now clear that the pattern of energy provision, the relationship between energy consumption and economic development, and the choice between different energy systems are by no means self-evident matters. The arguments presented in a number of alternative energy forecasts for the UK and the politics of the emerging green movement both provide a new approach to these problems.

Alternative energy forecasts

The late 1970s saw the publication of a number of alternative energy forecasts and scenarios for the UK which were far more sophisticated than anything the 'alternatives' movement had previously produced. These studies gave, and continue to give, energy campaigning an important cutting edge in that they demonstrate, in some detail, the technical viability of possible alternative energy futures.

Three such studies considered here are: *An Alternative Energy Strategy for the UK* produced by the National Centre for Alternative Technology (NCAT) in 1977.[1] *A Low Energy Strategy for the UK* by Gerald Leach for the International Institute for Environment and Development (IIED) in 1979;[2] *Energy Options and*

Employment by Dave Elliot for the Centre for Alternative Industrial and Technological Systems (CAITS), also in 1979.[3]

More recently, the publication in 1983 by Earth Resources Research (ERR) of their detailed and comprehensive work, *Energy Efficient Futures*[4] (EEF) has taken the process one stage further. EEF is already being used as a source book by many energy activists and is likely to become a point of reference for future debate on energy policy. All four studies share a common approach in that they project into the future on the basis of current possibilities that are *not* being taken up. The major point of contrast comes in an area outside of the control of those who produced the scenarios. All the earlier studies were written and conceived during a period of Labour government, with Benn as Energy Minister – there was at least the possibility of a receptive hearing from government or from radical elements within the party of that government. EEF was also initiated during the life of the 1974-9 Labour administration. This is not a coincidence – the Department of Energy under Benn set out to encourage the production of just such independent assessments. Unfortunately, EEF was published into a very different political climate and is at present unlikely to influence government energy policy.

Alternative energy forecasts are invariably punctuated with a mass of statistical and technical information. This chapter summarizes and simplifies the important conclusions in the forecasts and concentrates more on social and economic implications than on technical details. Relevant technical data are presented in tabular form, both within the text and at the end of the chapter.

Energy forecasting
At the time the three earlier energy forecasts were produced (Leach, NCAT and Elliot), there was a growing realization among researchers that the correct way to make forecasts or construct scenarios was to start not with primary energy but with end-use energy.[5] Before this, energy forecasts (notably those by the Department of Energy) had been based on figures for primary energy. A fixed ratio between growth in gross domestic product (GDP) and growth in energy demand was almost invariably assumed. Then, using estimates for growth in GDP from

economic models, the primary energy demand growth was simply calculated. Forecasting thus consisted of extrapolating past energy-use patterns. This method provided the statistics behind the popular myth of the 'energy gap'[6] which was used as one of the justifications for the necessity of nuclear power. It failed to take into account many important changes in energy use. Energy conservation effects and improved energy efficiencies in equipment were not allowed for, neither was the change in the economy away from energy-intensive manufacturing to service industries. While it appeared during the 1950s and 1960s that a link between GDP growth and energy demand actually existed, since the 1970s any such correlation has broken down and the assumption has quite clearly been disproved.

The only way to take into account efficiency of energy use in industry or at home, and to gauge the effect of the introduction of conservation methods, is to adopt the 'bottom-up' method – starting calculations with energy end-use. This approach is very complicated and detailed since the end-uses have to be broken down into as many different parts as possible. Effects of conservation and improved efficiency can then be properly measured on each separate end-use. This was the approach taken by both Leach and ERR.

Primary energy demand

The growth in the sophistication of the modelling of energy use, coupled with changes in energy consumption and declining economic growth, has over the last decade had its effect on government forecasts. Since 1976 they have been steadily falling, as shown in the official forecasts for primary energy demand in the year 2000:

1976	760 mtce[7]
June 1977	500 - 600 mtce[8]
Oct. 1977	450 - 560 mtce[9]
1979	445 - 515 mtce[10]

The CEGB forecast, presented to the Sizewell 'B' Inquiry in 1982, was for between 250 and 410 mtce.[11] For reference, primary demand in recent years has been:

1976   363 mtce or 9350 PJ[12]
1980   344.7 mtce or 8859 PJ[13]

This was made up as follows:

Table 6.1 Actual primary energy demand – in petajoules

Fuel	1976	1980
Coal	3,187	3,105
Oil	4,167	3,531
Natural gas	1,536	1,827
Nuclear	441	396
Hydro		
Solar		
Wind		
Wave	19	n/a
Tidal		
Geothermal		
Biomass		
Other		
Total renewables	19	
Total	**9,350**	**8,859**

N.B. ERR defines 1 mtce as 25.7 PJ. This is adopted here and in subsequent tables in this chapter. All other figures in these tables have been converted accordingly. 1976 figures from ERR, *Energy Efficient Futures*, p. xv. 1980 figures from Department of Energy, *Proof of Evidence for the Sizewell 'B' Public Inquiry*, Appendix 2.

In contrast, all of the 'alternative' scenarios involve radical changes from current energy policy and practice. They cannot be regarded as predictions of Britain's energy future nor as statements of what is likely to happen. The NCAT strategy, rather than forecasting the energy demand, set a target of primary energy demand and showed how this could be met. The strategy outlined by Elliot referred to only one sector of current energy demand, so avoiding the necessity of making predictions of total energy demand. Of the three 1970s studies, Leach provides the most comprehensive forecast in that he constructed models for energy consumption in Britain and then used them to find future energy demand, assuming an extensive conservation programme. The ERR study took Leach's approach much further, presenting four possible future energy scenarios and breaking end-use down into over 5,000 different categories, as compared to 400 in Leach's work.

The four alternatives

NCAT: An Alternative Energy Strategy for the UK By setting a target for primary energy demand in 2025,[14] this approach implicitly makes energy policy the most fundamental aspect of economic and social planning, and would involve subordinating the rest of the economy to meet the target set. The report attempted to play down the impact such an approach would have on industry and society, but it does in fact imply major social and economic changes.

Overall, the scenario aimed to end the need for nuclear power and to minimize the use of fossil fuels – with the exception of coal whose consumption was seen as increasing slightly from 1975 levels.[15] These changes were seen as being made possible by the development of renewable sources and conservation. The energy demand target was chosen as that which would provide approximately the same end-use energy in 2025 as in 1975.

Although no exact quantitative assumptions about economic growth are made in this scenario, it was suggested by the authors that a zero or low-growth economy is implied by such a programme. In order to avoid the unemployment that would accompany a low-growth strategy it was suggested that a large-scale restructuring of industry would be necessary. This is seen as encompassing a move towards smaller industries that could create new employment. The report hoped that the move to smaller-scale and decentralized energy sources might promote such a development.[16] Opportunities for exporting alternative energy technologies, and the direct employment possibilities implied by a developing alternative energy industry, are pointed out.[17]

The NCAT figures for primary energy demand in the year 2025 are extrapolated below:

Table 6.2 NCAT – primary energy demand in 2025 – in petajoules

Fuel	2025
Coal	4,112
Oil	—
Natural gas	—
Nuclear	—
Hydro	20
Solar	640
Wind	360
Wave	1,440
Tidal	40
Geothermal	—
Biomass	720
Other	—
Total renewables	3,220
Total	**7,332**

Extrapolated from the NCAT review of energy sources. N.B. Figures in this and the tables that follow are presented in order to illustrate the range of possible options and the differing options with regard to the balance of different energy resources in energy provision. All of the figures are speculative, some of them were prepared nearly a decade ago – they should *not* be regarded as predictions, up to date forecasts or proposals by their respective authors.

Elliot: Energy Options and Employment   This study is an estimate of the cost, and the employment generated, from a limited investment programme in conservation and renewable energy sources. The proposed programme would save approximately 30 per cent of primary energy demand at the time of the study, comparable to the primary energy contribution of a 40 GW nuclear power programme (that proposed by the UKAEA to the Royal Commission on Environmental Pollution, the Flowers Commission in 1976).[18]

Elliot estimated that his alternative programme would generate well over twice as many jobs as the nuclear programme up to the year 2000, at approximately two-thirds of the cost.[19]

This scenario has a more limited timescale than the others, considered only up to the end of the century – although, as Elliot suggested, it could be regarded as the first stage of a large programme comparable to the NCAT scenario. Bearing this in mind, Elliot briefly outlined a more radical programme to run until 2025, where the contribution from renewables and the savings from conservation measures add up to 65 per cent of 'current' (i.e. 1979) primary energy demand. The programmes for conservation, CHP, solar energy, wind energy and wave energy would be extended by adopting already-proposed possibilities by workers in these various fields. Combined with conservation methods in transport, industry, solar cell technology and tidal and geothermal contributions, plus an ambitious heat pump programme, a total saving of over 110 per cent of 'current' primary energy demand is suggested, i.e. conservation, energy efficiency and new energy technologies combine to add up to energy inputs and savings *greater* than existing primary energy demand.[20] Elliot's programme for renewables, linked to official assumptions of the production levels for oil, gas and coal, could more than meet the highest projections for energy demand in the year 2000.[21]

Because of the limited aim of the main scenario – to calculate the employment generated by an 'alternative' as opposed to a nuclear programme – there are no explicit assumptions about economic growth. However, Elliot did suggest that the type of scenario discussed would imply industrial decentralization and descaling. Although he argued that a move in this direction would generate more employment, Elliot suggested that if high unemployment is to be avoided in the long term, a major reconstruction of the whole economic and social system is necessary.[22]

Elliot's figures for primary energy demand in the year 2025 are extrapolated below (from the 'radical programme'):

Table 6.3 Elliot – Primary Energy Demand in 2025 – in petajoules

Fuel	2025
Hydro	—
Solar	850
Wind	170
Wave	2,500
Tidal	250
Geothermal	85
Biomass	590
Other	—
Ren. total	4,445

Extrapolated from Elliot's 'radical programme'. No figures for fossil fuels or total primary energy demand are given.

Leach: a Low Energy Strategy for the UK   Leach's scenario is by far the most detailed of the three written in the 1970s. It provided a complete model for possible future energy uses in the UK up until 2025, from end-uses to primary demand, with extensive breakdowns by fuels and usage.

The aim of the study was to show that a comprehensive programme of energy conservation could lead to continued economic growth and prosperity without necessitating an increase in primary energy demand by 2025.[23] The introduction of renewable energy sources was almost completely ignored, so that by 2025 they are seen as providing 8-9 per cent only of primary energy demand (excluding hydro).[24] The point of this was to emphasize what could be achieved simply by the use of available technology in the field of conservation, not because of any doubt concerning the importance of renewable energy sources.

The strategy assumed that there would be continued economic growth right up until 2025. The study was split into two cases – a high-growth scenario and a low-growth one. In the high-growth scenario the economy was assumed to grow steadily up until 2025, when it would be three times its 1975 size. These assumptions are in accordance with the 1978 forecast of the Department of Energy in Energy Paper 29. In the low-growth scenario the economy expands in the same way – following trends from the 1960s – up until about 2000, after which growth tails off. In 2025 the economy would be twice its size at the time of the study.

This growth – now most unlikely after the experience of the last decade – would have meant little change in the structure of British industry. Many of the conservation methods were designed to be economically attractive in such a situation with lit-

Table 6.4 Leach – Primary Energy demand in 2025 – in petajoules

Fuel	Low Growth 2025	High Growth 2025
Coal	3,290	3,804
Oil	2,107	2,570
Nat. Gas	951	1,079
Nuclear	565	720
Hydro	51	51
Solar	157	190
Wind	116	146
Wave	234	293
Tidal	—	—
Geothermal	—	—
Biomass	—	—
Other	100	108
Ren. total	658	788
Total	**7,582**	**8,969**

Converted from Leach, *Low Energy Strategy*, p. 188.

tle or no government subsidy. Writing now, in the mid-1980s, faced with high unemployment and the rapid decline of the traditional manufacturing industry over the last five years, this strategy has a lot less to offer than it did when Leach presented it. One effect of the recession is that conservation technologies are unlikely to be adopted by hard-pressed companies without unprecedented government intervention. Similarly, as building programmes are cut back, so heat-saving measures are unlikely to be implemented.

ERR: energy-efficient futures   The ERR study contrasts a future based on nuclear energy, coal and oil imports with one based on a renewable energy system.

The study presents four possible future energy scenarios. Two of these are described as 'technical fix futures' with rising material living standards and high economic growth. The other two are 'conserver society futures' with a lower growth rate and the emergence of life styles and policies that are more compatible with environmental conservation.[25] In these cases the economy is described as 'post-industrial' – an imprecise term implying not an absence of any kind of 'industry' but only a shift away from the traditional manufacturing and heavy engineering industries. In each category a scenario assuming a high degree of energy-efficiency improvements is contrasted with a scenario assuming a slower change in the same direction.

All four scenarios are based on the following assumptions about energy policy: a high priority is placed on

'1. A rapid and wide-ranging programme of improvements in energy efficiency.

2. A gradual phasing in of renewable energy sources.

3. A sharp reduction in the depletion rate of the UK's oil and natural gas resources.

4. The phasing out of nuclear energy.

5. Virtual self-sufficiency in energy.'[26]

The technical fix scenarios follow the assumptions of the Department of Energy (EP39 – 1979) on economic growth – little change in economic and industrial structure and a growth in GDP by a factor of 2.9 between 1976 and 2025.

The conserver society scenarios assume changes in attitude,

life style and economic structure, with a shift away from heavy industry and towards electronics and computers, information processing, communications systems, research, education and services. Economic growth is assumed to be 1 per cent per year up to 2000 and 0 per cent thereafter. It is argued that this is consistent with rising productivity and full employment *if* the working week is reduced.[27]

The study acknowledges that the technical fix scenarios are making an unrealistic assessment of future possibilities. GDP in 1982 was barely higher than in 1976 – requiring a growth rate of over 5 per cent per year from 1983-90 to catch up with the assumed rate.[28] The technical fix scenarios thus provide a useful point of comparison with official studies in terms of energy consumption, but do not indicate a future which is likely to occur.

Table 6.5 ERR – Primary energy demand in 2025 – in petajoules

Fuel	Tech. fix, high energy efficiency	Tech. fix, low energy efficiency	Conserver, high energy efficiency	Conserver, low energy efficiency
Coal	820	2,203	445	1,203
Oil	858	1,834	317	916
Nat. Gas	297	589	132	393
Nuclear	—	—	—	—
Hydro	38	38	26	25
Solar	873	302	220	250
Wind	133	116	87	58
Wave	—	18	—	12
Tidal	—	44	—	29
Geothermal	269	243	179	183
Biomass	1,580	890	1,029	610
Other	—	—	—	—
Ren. total	2,893	1,651	1,541	1,167
Total	**4,868**	**6,282**	**2,449**	**3,679**

Source: ERR, *Energy Efficient Futures*, p. xv.

Far more likely is a future in which even the scale of technical improvements in the energy field envisaged here could not offset the ill effects of a failed attempt to restore high economic growth – seen by ERR as 'unemployment, regional depression, rising social and political conflicts'.[29] The study poses the conserver society as an alternative to this bleak future.

The report breaks energy use down into about 5,000 categories and assesses the role that energy efficiency and renewable energy sources could play during the years leading up to 2025.

All four ERR scenarios suggest a major shift away from fossil fuels and towards renewable technologies, particularly solar, wind, geothermal and biomass. Nuclear power is phased out completely. In the technical fix scenarios it is illustrated that primary energy demand could fall by between 30-50 per cent by 2025, despite high economic growth. In the conserver society scenarios the fall is even greater, between 60-75 per cent with the consequence that fossil fuels are used even less.[30]

The approaches compared

Each of these four studies approach the energy question from a slightly different direction and illustrate different points. Leach presented a strong case for conservation, all other factors (except the rate of growth of GDP) remaining unchanged. Both NCAT and Elliot, in contrast, implicitly challenged profitability as the main criteria for production decisions – NCAT emphasizing instead the energy target and Elliot emphasizing job creation. The ERR study also illustrates that for a range of contrasting economic developments major energy savings are technically possible.

Different assumptions about economy and society are implied in each study. Both Leach and the NCAT study accepted that the *option* of sustained high economic growth was possible for British capitalism. Leach, at least by implication, also saw it as desirable and spoke of a 'prosperous low-energy future'.[31] The implications of his message can be summed up as a lot more conservation, a lot less nuclear power and no other fundamental changes. The NCAT study, in contrast, argued that even high economic growth cannot solve structural unemployment, and

Table 6.6 Energy strategies compared

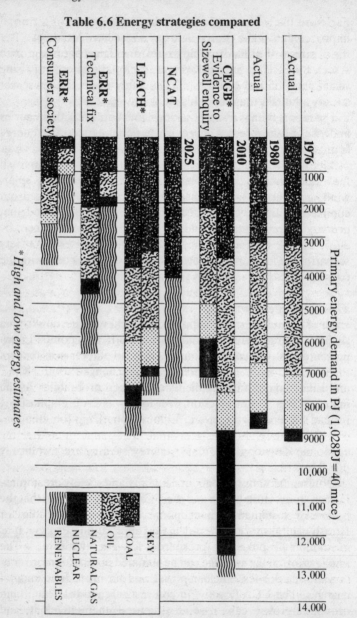

*High and low energy estimates

Primary energy demand in PJ (1,028PJ = 40 mtce)

KEY
RENEWABLES
NUCLEAR
NATURAL GAS
OIL
COAL

discussed the problems involved in changing *by choice* from a high-growth to a low-growth or even zero-growth economy. The conclusion was drawn that 'if the present structure of industry survives the energy changes envisaged it is likely that a hard core of unemployment will accompany it'.[32] It is ironic that less than a decade later this situation has arisen unbidden, and with no positive accompanying changes in the energy field. Contrary to NCAT's assumptions, Leach's study illustrated that relatively high economic growth and a low-energy strategy could be compatible – a fundamental point for the formation of energy policy.

Overall, though, events in the economic and political arena have left these latter two studies wrong-footed only a few years after their publication. With hindsight their fault appears to be in holding a static view of how British capitalism will 'naturally' operate based on the historically unique period of the 1960s and early 1970s. Leach assumes that with favourable government and the right technical inputs growth can continue unabated; NCAT takes the view that the growth juggernaut will have to be stopped in order to preserve energy resources, but sees this as likely to come about only through the conscious development of an alternative energy strategy. Elliot's study avoids these errors in the main by concentrating on illustrating a specific point about employment possibilities, and as such his arguments retain more relevance today, although the statistics necessarily need updating.

The ERR study ventures further than the other three in considering what kind of social fabric might accompany its radical conservation policies. This is a valuable exercise but it is at this point that a major weakness of the ERR study becomes clear. The ERR 'conserver society' is radically different from Britain a we know it today, incorporating decentralization of government with democratic participation at a local level, a rejection of authority, hierarchy and class distinctions, and an increase in the accountability of large companies with resources and returns on investment put to socially useful purposes. It is further seen as involving changes in life style and economic structure away from heavy industry and towards information industries and services.[33] The study does not consider the social forces that would carry out such changes nor the resistance that might be encountered. On the one hand, it assumes an extension of popular control over resources, with production decisions based on factors other than the profit motive; on the other, private capital is evidently left intact and operating within a market economy necessarily based on competition and profit. Within this situation it is assumed, incredibly, that whilst 'class inequalities' will still be a source of conflict, this will largely be in the area of 'relative disparities in living standards' and will be reduced in time through redistribution and improved education opportunities.[34]

The conserver society scenario avoids assessing how much gradual social, economic and environmental reform capitalism and capitalists would accept. It transposes radical social and technical changes onto the existing capitalist framework – changes which go *beyond* the parameters within which that framework can operate. In this situation, in fact, class conflict would arise primarily over the control of productive resources rather than over relative differences in living standards. The likelihood is surely that the ruling class would respond viciously and effectively to any such threat to their power and position.

By trying to reconcile energy efficiency with capitalist production the study is forced to insist that capital can be 'tamed' and still remain capital.

Despite their differences and shortcomings, all four studies nonetheless illustrate the immense *technical* possibilities available to us. It is clear that without material hardship the energy infrastructure *could* be radically transformed. Basic energy needs could be met at the same time as drastically reducing the consumption of energy resources and the damaging effect of energy provision on the environment. It is not through an absence of alternative options that British energy provision relies increasingly on oil and nuclear power. It is through a refusal to take those options up.

The Green movement

By speculating on the social factors involved in radical technical change, the ERR study moves into the field addressed by Green politics. Radical changes in energy policy play an important part in any Green approach. Unfortunately EEF's failure to integrate the conflict between labour and capital into its strategy is reflected in the approach of the major Green theorists who have influenced the British scene.

'Green' has come to be the word used to imply a general concern for the environment. Even the SDP have Green candidates – notably Tom Burke (formerly director of Friends of the Earth), who stood as a parliamentary candidate in Brighton Kemptown in the 1983 general election. As such, in political dialogue, it has all but replaced 'environmental' or even 'ecological' as a way of referring to policies and strategies. In this sense it loses much of its specific 'Green' meaning – if all the major parties have Green policies, if Green is a euphemism for any minor tinkering with existing practice, then it is simply a new word for describing an old approach.

Green, of course, is much more than this – for the Green movement specifically defines itself as beyond minor reforms, beyond mere tinkering. Green for the Greens implies a complete philosophy, embracing all aspects of human life on earth. It is a holistic approach to the world ecology and to the interface between human populations, their socioeconomic systems and that ecology. In short, Green politics implies smallness of scale, an emphasis on self-awareness, planetary awareness and non-violence, sustainable economies based on renewable or recyclable resources, and an overall commitment to harmonious human relations and a complementary relationship between society and the environment.

Broadly speaking, Green politics also implies deemphasizing class struggle or class-based politics and looking instead at change through a major shift in perception and through an unprecedented development of consensus across and overriding class divisions. This is particularly true in Britain.

The Ecology Party manifesto of 1983 stated quite clearly that 'the old-fashioned politics of class conflict are grinding to a halt';[35] that we must move from the 'politics of class interests to the politics of life interests'.[36] The same theme emerges in Jonathon Porritt's (Director of Friends of the Earth, former chair of the Ecology Party) *Seeing Green* where class divisions are seen as 'notional' products of an 'old-fashioned' way of seeing the world.[37]

Porritt's arguments are, in part, derived from Fritjof Capra, the American nuclear physicist and theorist of the 'New Age'. Capra takes a similar approach in *The Turning Point*,[38] seeing Marx as placing too much emphasis on conflict and disputing the central role given by Marx to class struggle in social change.[39] At the core of Capra's approach is the idea that the world's current state of ecological and social disorder derives, in the first instance, from the dominant world view through which reality is conceptualized. This world view is broadly described as 'mechanistic' and is traced back to early developments in Western science and Western thought. Greatly simplified, this mechanistic 'paradigm' can be understood as living and understanding the world through dividing it up and dominating it. In contrast, the new holistic paradigm operates through unifying and complementing the whole.

For Capra, change from the old to the new paradigm is an inevitable and natural process.[40] A process which will bring with it revolutionary changes in culture and society – and of course in energy provision.

Within this framework, class distinctions are simply part of the old fashioned system of division and domination that will, in time pass away. It follows that to identify with one class or another is simply to get caught in a conceptual trap.

Porritt is more pragmatic in his approach than Capra and places more emphasis on specific social policies, but his message is essentially the same. The central problem in *Seeing Green* becomes 'industrialism' – a concept which is little more than a description of industrial society as it appears to be, but with the assumption that this system is maintained primarily by the way people think. The pursuit of conventional economic growth at high social and environmental cost is thus seen as continuing essentially because people believe in it. It follows from this that radical change in the pattern of belief would lead to 'industrialism's' inevitable decline.

These assumptions underpin the problems already identified

in the work of ERR, problems which are similarly to be found in the 1983 Ecology Party manifesto – a document on which Porritt himself had a considerable influence.

Both documents are impressive, both are well researched and detailed, both address issues of social policy and put forward challenging alternatives to existing practice. Neither takes the necessary step of asking *how* a transition to these new policies might come about.

In the light of the idealism that evidently provides British Green politics with its theoretical basis, these omissions are not surprising. In so far as the documents are seen as contributing towards an awareness of Capra's inevitable 'rising culture', they are doing all that seems necessary.

Other Green theorists, notably André Gorz, Rudolf Bahro and Murray Bookchin, approach the issue of ecology and social change with a greater awareness of the problems discussed here. Similarly, the German Green movement has a strong anti-capitalist element within it. But it does not appear that the self-identified UK Greens active in local groups, ecology parties and so on have taken many of these influences on board. Capra and Porritt express ideas that have taken root in the movement and which continue to inform most of its activities. The best prospects for the development of a socialist Green politics appear to lie in the Socialist Environment and Resources Association's (SERA's) growing influence in this field.[41]

A socialist approach

At the core of a socialist approach is an analysis of capitalism which sees it as a material reality quite distinct from the concept of 'industrialism' developed by Porritt and others.

Central to this analysis is the concept of 'class' (outlined in the introduction to this book) and the acknowledgement that the interests of the working class and the ruling class are fundamentally and dynamically opposed. This distinction of classes is not determined by the way people think about themselves, but by their relationship to the process of production and distribution. While it is true that popular beliefs contribute to the continuation of this situation, it will take more than a change in beliefs to wrest power from those who currently hold it. Individuals within the ruling class may undergo radical changes in their approach to the world, but the class as a whole is bound to continue striving in mutual competition for profit and, as a consequence, for growth.

There is no precedent in known history of a class *as a whole* simply volunteering to give up its powers and privileges, and this implies that change will necessarily come only *through* conflict.

Exactly what form this conflict will take is not an issue here – what is significant is simply that plans for radical social change must take the inevitability of class conflict into account. Indeed, reasserting Marx as against Capra, it will be through such conflict that change will occur. The immense technical possibilities illustrated by the alternative energy forecasts and the visions of a new future that inspire the Green movement do however leave the official labour movement looking sadly old-fashioned and uninspired. The critique developed in this chapter should be tempered by the knowledge that radical changes in energy provision have yet to appear on the agenda of the Labour Party or TUC.

PART 3

7. Energy and society

The implication of many of the 'alternative' forecasts discussed in Chapter 6 is that energy policy at present is short-sighted and irrational, and that it can be changed simply through a process of education or by merely demonstrating the viability of new options. This position ignores certain problems.

The energy infrastructure in any society is fundamental to social and economic life, integrally linked to the organization of production. Significant changes in energy policy inevitably imply changes in the deep structure of society, changes which can only be seen as a challenge to those vested interests which benefit from existing arrangements.

If we are to develop a new approach to energy planning and energy use – a democratic and socialist approach – then it is vital to have a clear understanding of the dynamics of energy use in this society, indeed throughout human history.

Energy in society

Anthropologists have traditionally defined humans as tool-making primates. By making and using implements, humans act upon their environment in a unique way and launch themselves upon a unique process of development. It now seems likely that a plant-gathering, tool-using hominid lifestyle developed in East Africa between 5 and 8 million years ago, which stimulated, and was stimulated by, other characteristics, such as bipedalism and the use of language.[1] A process was sparked off whereby development in one of these areas encouraged further development in the others. Humanity did not simply adjust to the environment, but progressively acquired the ability to act collectively upon it.

It thus launched itself upon a trajectory of cultural development which was dictated not by any logic of 'natural equilibrium', but by the logic of cumulative change. This implied not merely the transformation of the natural environment, but the progressive self-transformation of humanity: 'By thus acting on the external world and changing it, (Man) at the same time changes his own nature'[2] (*sic*)

Simple tool use does not in itself represent the harnessing of any external source of energy. The energy available to Palaeolithic ('Old Stone Age') society was simply the muscular energy of humans themselves, derived most immediately from plant and animal foods, and ultimately, via photosynthesis, from the sun. The making and usage of cutting, digging, poking and carrying tools did not in itself add to the sum total of available social energy. However, it did enable that energy to be used more efficiently, to be enhanced and focused in a multitude of ways. The activities of tool making and tool use, which define humanity itself, therefore imply a rudimentary level of conscious enhancement of the energy available to early society.

Palaeolithic gatherer-hunter society was succeeded in some parts of the world by a Neolithic ('New Stone Age') 'revolution'. Neolithic society was based not upon naturally occurring food sources within a given range, but upon agriculture and the domestication of animals: in other words, upon a deliberately controlled, deliberately husbanded food supply. Agriculture and domestic animals did not make available more energy per capita than was available to Palaeolithic society, except insofar as draught animals were used for heavy loads. Neolithic society was still dependent essentially upon muscular energy derived from the sun and the soil. The crucial difference, however, is that the development of agriculture increased the *productivity* of the soil. It produced a far greater volume of food per acre than would occur naturally, and thus supported a much higher density of population. With Neolithic society came the first large settled communities, the appearance of urban arts and crafts, and a new complexity in political and religious institutions.

Neither Palaeolithic nor Neolithic societies were 'in harmony' with the natural environment in some romantic sense. It may be popular and comforting to imagine that these apparently 'simple' communities enjoyed a natural ecological equilibrium, but this assumption would be very misleading. Human society is *defined* by its action upon the environment, and that action inevitably rebounds upon, and transforms, humanity itself. In this sense, human society always implies *dis*harmony with 'Nature'.

On the other hand, this must not be taken to mean that all societies necessarily ravage their natural environments. Gatherer-hunter societies do not damage their environment through over-population or overexploitation simply because they are too small to have such an impact. If natural food sources are not available, then people either migrate or face famine until the balance of resources is restored.[3] The environmental harmlessness of these societies is explained not by reference to an intrinsic lost virtue, but by their smallness of scale and simplicity of technology. Despite this smallness, gatherer-hunter communities often enjoy an affluent and leisured life style, and it is important to appreciate that they are coherent social formations in their own right, living on the basis of accumulated wisdom and not to be seen as societies which somehow 'failed' to develop into something else.

With the Neolithic and subsequent more complex forms of society, human action upon the environment became more drastic, leading to many examples of major change and sometimes to crisis or collapse. In the river valleys of the Tigris, Euphrates and Nile, the very survival of early agricultural society depended upon great civil engineering projects to drain marshes, control flooding and irrigate the soil.[4] Later, the Roman Empire was immensely parasitic upon the environment, and it has been suggested that deforestation may have contributed to the Empire's fall.[5]

Later still, in England, the clearing of the forests was a necessary prelude to widespread settlement. From the fifth century onwards, enormous swathes of forest land were felled, cleared and planted, and England took on an appearance which it largely retains today.[6] All of these are examples of major environmental change brought about by societies without any source of mechanical energy save the muscular energy of humans and domesticated animals.

The scope for action upon the environment was greatly increased once it became possible to harness external mechanical energy sources. As we saw above, the development of agriculture and animal husbandry represented not the tapping of a *new* source, but increased productivity of that most fundamental energy source, the food supply. Socially available energy was still, however, mediated through the muscle and sinew of living creatures. The genuine harnessing of external mechanical energy only came in the early Middle Ages.

The water mill was apparently known in ancient times and is described by a Greek writer,[7] but it only came to be widely used in Europe in medieval times, from the eleventh century, and it should rightly be regarded as a medieval device. Europe at this time was by no means the exclusive centre of technological development: methods for converting the water mill's rotary action to reciprocal motion (hammering, etc.) came from China.[8] Windmills also appeared in Europe in the twelfth century, either as a result of indigenous development or as imports from Iran,[9] and tidal power was being harnessed from the twelfth and thirteenth centuries. By 1200, therefore, wind, tide and river energy was being tapped, and this represented a *qualitative* technological advance of great significance.

For the first time, human society was drawing upon energy sources beyond the muscle power of living creatures. The technological advance of the early Middle Ages did not, of course, occur in isolation. This was a period of enormous creativity, dynamism and expansion. Trade routes locked the Christian and Muslim worlds into a fertile symbiosis. Economic activity and populations expanded, leading in England to a new spate of forest clearance. This vibrant epoch was only brought to an end by the Black Death, which killed over 30 per cent of the population of Europe in the mid-fourteenth century.[10]

The first stage of the Industrial Revolution in the eighteenth century was based upon these medieval energy sources. Up to 1800, water power was overwhelmingly the most important energy source for the cotton mills and iron works of England. While steam-engines were pioneered in the eighteenth century, it was not until well into the nineteenth that they replaced water power as the primary industrial source of motive power.[11]

One major point emerges from this brief survey of energy use in human history. A common bond links all human societies in that they all draw upon the collective ingenuity, mobility and dexterity of human beings to act upon the natural environment, potentially to transform it, and thus to transform themselves. Certain more complex social formations, such as those in the industrial West, are able to accelerate this process by harnessing enormous sources of external energy. This does not make us 'better' than gatherer-hunter communities, but it does make us more powerful.

It may be tempting when faced with the monumental potential destructiveness of modern capitalism to hark back to other, 'simpler' societies, to imagine that they enjoyed a natural environmental equilibrium which we have lost. But we cannot simply renounce the whole historical process which has brought us to this point. It is not that such a renunciation is 'wrong': it is simply impossible.

The historical development of human culture has been marked by the increasingly sophisticated harnessing of energy resources – not in the sense of a smooth progressive continuity, but in a sense of sporadic leaps forward which, having been made, are irrevocable. The Neolithic period was one such leap forward; the early Middle Ages another. The tapping of external sources of mechanical energy in the eleventh and twelfth centuries – water power, wind power and tidal power – is of especial significance because it opened the way for new levels of productivity, contributed to the emergence of a world market, and thus laid the foundations for capitalism.[12] The availability of non-muscular energy sources allowed humanity to move on from the use of mere tools to the use of machines,[13] and it is the development of machine technology which marks the emergence of the capitalist system of production.

Capital and energy

Viewed at a world level, capitalism is not driven by the fulfilment of human need, nor even by any long-term commitment to its own survival. The system proceeds, blindly, in the pursuit of profit. It is viable only so long as there are certain sectors of productive activity which can continue to realize an adequate rate of profit, an adequate return on investment, and which can thus provide a focus for overall accumulation and economic growth. Capitalism is, in other words, an immensely *dynamic* system of production: it must grow or die, it cannot survive in a state of equilibrium. At the same time, it is characterized by a *lack of overall planning*; its dynamism depends on competition between many individual enterprises, all of them operating on relatively short-term criteria.[14]

Underlying this inherent instability in the operations of capital is an even more fundamental contradiction in the conflict between capital and labour. Even when capitalism is 'working', growing at its most dynamic, this conflict remains and often indeed intensifies. The class struggle is conventionally understood as a series of battles over wages, hours and conditions of work. At another level, however, it is a battle over energy resources.

The growth of the system as a whole is rooted in the efforts of individual enterprises to secure advantage over each other in the market by relative improvements in productivity. This means investment in more sophisticated machinery at the relative expense of labour. Within individual firms, the balance of productive assets tends to shift away from living human labour towards 'dead' or 'accumulated' labour vested in machines.[15]

In energy terms, this means the replacement of the muscular and intellectual energy of living human beings by other forms of energy delivered as fuel to drive machines. The capitalist process of economic development therefore implies a very direct and specific impact on society's energy systems. It involves a shift away from human energy derived from food, and a shift towards external inputs derived either from renewable or finite sources.[16]

The actual consequence of this – the consequence of an economic system based on unplanned growth – is a steadily rising level of primary energy consumption. In theory this does not *have* to happen: rising consumption of useful energy could be sustained, while holding down primary energy inputs, *so long as* constant attention is paid to improving the efficiency of energy conversion, delivery and use. But the reality is that capitalism, in its restless search for expansion and profit, has no interest in energy efficiency as such. Specific circumstances may arise in which individual firms find it profitable to improve their energy efficiency – but not the system as a whole. The pattern is further consolidated by the fact that the energy sector itself is a key area of capitalist growth. Energy corporations – among the most powerful in the world – depend on continued rising energy consumption and continued dependence on their products. The result is that as capitalist growth continues, primary energy consumption steadily rises.

This is demonstrated by the figures. In 1950 world primary energy consumption was 50 per cent higher than in 1929; and in 1976 it was three times greater than in 1950.[17] Despite the recession, despite industrial decline and unemployment in the advanced capitalist countries and widening poverty in the underdeveloped countries, world primary energy consumption is *still* rising. It is important to remember that 'recession' means not that growth has stopped, but rather that it is proceeding at a pace generally regarded as unacceptable. It has been suggested that even a disastrously low level of economic growth to 2000 would still call for an annual 0.8 per cent increase in primary energy consumption.[18]

This steady increase is explained not only by gross expansion of economic activity, but also by changing patterns of energy supply. There is a clear tendency to deliver an increasing proportion of energy to the consumer in 'high-grade' form. As we have seen already, the capitalist system of production is characterized by dynamism and expansion but also by lack of overall planning. To thrive, it requires an environment in which capital accumulation can proceed, unhindered as far as possible by natural, social or technical obstacles. This has implications for factors as diverse as the labour market, the transport infrastructure and the credit system – and also for energy. Capital requires energy supply which is as *secure*, and yet as *flexible*, as possible. Security is essential to create a climate of confidence in which investment can take place. Flexibility is equally essential because capital's competitive and fragmented nature means that individual enterprises must be free to compete by pursuing different, inherently unpredictable lines of technical innovation. The energy supply system must allow for these different options by supplying energy in as flexible and universally applicable a form as possible. A restrictive energy supply system – a system based, for instance, exclusively on the heat content of coal or wood – restricts the technical options to capital, restricts the opportunities for competition and accumulation, and therefore threatens the expansion and survival of the system itself.

At different historical epochs, the requirement for high-grade flexible delivered energy has meant different things. In the nineteenth century, steam power replaced water power as the main industrial energy source in England. Steam power is a higher-grade form than water power. Whereas the useful energy of a water mill is directly dependent on the flow of the stream and is restricted in location, steam power is a secondary energy form derived from a primary source (coal) and is both *adjustable* and *mobile*. It can deliver the same amount of useful energy, in the same place as a water mill, but it can also deliver much more useful energy in many more places. Steam power therefore opens up new possibilities for industrial development and expansion.

Today, the most flexible high-grade energy form is electricity. Electricity is an immensely convenient fuel. It can be generated from renewable, fossil fuel or nuclear power stations. It can be transmitted across vast distances to be delivered at a place far from its point of generation. It can be used to supply heat, light, mechanical or electronic energy. Its technical attractions are self-evident.

There is, however, a price to be paid. High-grade energy may be flexible, but only because it is the end result of a series of transformations worked upon the original primary fuel input. A conventional coal-fired power station burns coal to heat water, produce steam, drive turbines, generate electricity. The final useful energy available to the consumer is only a fraction of the energy potential in the coal because of conversion losses at each stage of the operation. These losses can certainly be reduced by engineering advances, but only up to a point: there are absolute thermodynamic limits to the efficiency of power stations.[19]

On top of the energy costs of conversion, high-grade energy also demands energy costs to maintain a supportive industrial infrastructure. A functioning electricity supply system requires large-scale mining for coal and other minerals, plus engineering, metal manufacturing and construction industries. Britain's electricity supply industry is in fact the country's largest *consumer* of primary energy.[20]

Despite all these costs, electricity's flexibility and convenience makes it highly attractive for capital and an increasing proportion of energy is delivered as electricity, both nationally and internationally, as described in Chapter 3. In Britain, primary energy consumption rose by 25 per cent between 1960 and 1976, but energy *delivered*, on a heat-supplied basis rose by only 13 per cent. In other words, energy was being used much less efficiently in 1976 than in 1960. The explanation is that more energy was being delivered as electricity, incurring major losses in the process of generation, transmission and delivery. In fact, the rise in total energy consumption during the 1960s can be explained not in terms of rising real demand, but in terms of the greater inefficiency incurred by the shift to electricity. From 1960 to 1976, electricity doubled as a percentage of total delivered energy.[21]

In the world as a whole, the trend is even more dramatic. Between 1960 and 1976, world energy consumption doubled,[22] but in roughly the same period world electricity production trebled.[23] Detailed analysis would, of course, reveal very different rates of growth, and different energy balances, between different countries, but the overall tendency for electricity to increase its share of energy supply is clear.

This expansion of electricity is planned to continue. In the UK, the Department of Energy expects electricity to rise as a proportion of final energy demand from its 1980 level of 14 per cent to perhaps 23 per cent by 2010.[24] More widely, the International Energy Agency has found that in the advanced capitalist countries as a group electricity is projected to grow faster than any other energy form to 2000, at a rate equal to or above that of the economy. [25] If electricity use grows this fast in the advanced capitalist countries, then the experience of the past two decades suggests an even more rapid expansion in the developing countries.

These global trends may sometimes seem to be contradicted by specific, local events. For some companies, energy efficiency is clearly desirable as a way of keeping down costs and there is, in fact, a steady demand for conservation equipment. From this, it might appear that there is no necessary contradiction between capitalist logic and energy efficiency, and the claim that capitalism means rising energy consumption might appear farfetched. However, the logic of the system as a whole cannot be grasped by looking at the behaviour of individual firms or even individual countries. Capitalism is, after all, an unplanned system, allowing nooks and crannies within which opportunities may be pursued which would not be acceptable on a larger scale.

The system must be viewed as a whole, as a global network of productive activity with its own logic and dynamic. At *this* level there is no sign of energy efficiency being pursued as a priority – on the contrary, all the trends are towards rising primary energy consumption and the delivery of an increasing proportion of energy in the high-grade form of electricity, with all its attendant energy costs. As a system of production based on unplanned growth, capitalism cannot restructure itself around the efficient use of energy. Such a restructuring would imply detailed and co-ordinated planning and a careful matching of resources to projected needs which would deny to capital the dynamic, irresponsible freedom which is its very essence. It would restrict capital's options for growth, freeze its mobility and impose upon it an alien set of social and environmental obligations.

If energy efficiency is to be pursued as a valuable goal in its own right, it can only be developed as a political initiative with its roots *outside* the logic of capitalist growth and profitability. There would however be resistance from capital in general to any attempt to impose an energy-efficient regime, and this resistance would be spearheaded by those large companies which currently dominate energy supply and which are counting on continued expansion along conventional lines. These firms simply have too much to lose.

To sum up: capitalism is a specific mode of production with its own logic and its own requirements. It makes certain characteristic demands upon the energy-supply sector and imposes certain patterns upon it. Any attempt to alter the nature and direction of energy policy must take into account the fact that its present structure is not accidental or arbitrary, but is both a reflection of, and a necessary condition for, the capitalist system of production.

Socialism and energy

If capitalism requires a particular structure of energy supply, the question immediately arises: does socialism offer anything different? There are many countries in the world which style themselves 'socialist' and which claim to pursue a path of economic development quite different from that of the capitalist countries. Inevitably, when the possibility of a distinctive 'socialist energy strategy' is raised, many people will look to these countries on the assumption that they provide a model of socialist energy policies in practice.

In trying to understand the relationship between socialism and energy, it is necessary to establish whether or not existing, avowedly socialist countries provide a valid model for us. The most useful example to take is the largest, longest-established and most powerful of these countries, the USSR.

Chapter 1 looked at current trends in Soviet energy policy, but a little historical background is relevant here. In 1920, when the civil war was coming to an end and economic reconstruction was the major priority, the Bolsheviks started to consider the realities of economic planning. In those early plans, the energy project known as 'GOELRO' was the central feature, bearing the personal approval and enthusiasm of Lenin himself. Lenin said: 'Communism is Soviet power plus electrification of the whole country, since industry cannot be developed without electrification.'[26] GOELRO was an ambitious project for the electrification of Russia and was seen as essential because of the primary significance of electricity for industry, agriculture and transport. From that period onwards, electrification has been taken as one of the key indicators of Soviet economic progress. It has increased steadily from 1920, not only in absolute terms but also as a proportion of overall energy supply. Growth in electricity output has always been at least twice as fast as growth in primary energy production, and in some periods it has been four or five times as fast.[27] In this pattern of steadily rising gross energy consumption, and in the rising proportion of energy delivered as electricity, the USSR's development mirrors that of both the advanced capitalist countries and the newly industrializing countries of the Third World.

At one level, then, Soviet development has clearly been driven by the same dynamics as development in the capitalist countries. Throughout the history of the USSR, there has been a very clear and conscious policy of copying and mastering capitalist technology in order to build the material basis for communism and to 'make good the distance' between it and the capitalist countries.[28] This emphasis has clearly been underpinned by a conception of science and technology as essentially *neutral*. For the Soviet leadership from Lenin onwards, economic development and technological progress were conceived of as developing along the same lines under socialism as under capitalism – but under socialism it was assumed that the development would be more rapid, more efficient and more equitable. In other words, the USSR has taken its technological cue from its major capitalist rivals and one result is that the Soviet energy sector has developed along lines similar to the energy sector in capitalist countries. It has prioritized expansion of supply rather than efficient end-use and the final result is energy wastage on a scale that matches that of capitalism.

Is this socialism? The USSR's claim to be a socialist country is often defended by pointing to its rapid economic development, to state ownership of the means of production and centralized state planning, and to the absence of an identifiable capitalist class. In this way socialism becomes identified with the rapid and large-scale development of the forces of production under centralized state planning. It would seem to follow logically that given a state-planned economy, growing quantitative output is seen as a good indicator of progress towards socialism and communism.

However, this conception of socialism deserves closer attention. Behind it lies an assumption that technological advance is a unilinear process, a one-way journey down a predetermined road. The issue of economic and technological development is thus reduced to a question of speed and centralization: any country which is industrializing rapidly on the basis of state planning might be regarded as 'socialist' according to this criterion.

It would certainly be a sterile exercise to set up some abstract ideal of 'socialism' and then seek to measure reality by this arbitrary yardstick; such a procedure would be contrary to the whole spirit of the socialist tradition. And yet it is important to respond to the crude and depressing conception of socialism set out above, which is a travesty of the socialism of Marx and Engels. Their essential starting point was that socialism must be understood as the logical and historical *successor* to capitalism. Socialism is that mode of production which transcends the limitations and contradictions of capitalism by building upon the economic and political foundations laid down *by* capitalism.[29]

This is not the experience of the USSR, which has established an industrial economy on a largely pre-capitalist base. Its social system has emerged not from the pressures of a mature capitalism driving up against its own contradictions; but rather from the pressures generated in the early twentieth century at the *periphery* of world capitalism, precisely where capital's penetration had been sporadic and localized and had failed to launch a thoroughgoing process of economic development. The social system in the USSR is not a successor to capitalism, not a resolution of capitalism's limitations, but rather an alternative non-capitalist road to industrialization. Its driving motive has not been to pick up where capital leaves off, but rather to run alongside.

The fact that Soviet energy patterns have followed a very similar trajectory to that of the capitalist countries is therefore not surprising, nor is the USSR's conscious reproduction of capitalist technological priorities. It also follows that Soviet energy policy is not a reliable guide to the likely structure of a *socialist* energy policy, whether in Britain or anywhere else. In order to establish the parameters of such a socialist policy, let us return to and reinterpret that essential point made above. Capitalist social relations place obstacles on the development of the forces of production; socialist social relations will remove those obstacles and allow the fuller development of the forces of production. If, as now seems clear, the 'fuller development of the forces of production' is not to be understood in crude quantitative terms, then what does it mean?

A closer look at the nature of capitalist production helps to answer this question. Capitalist growth depends not merely on a vast outpouring of commodities onto the marketplace. It also forces individual enterprises into a constant process of choice, of choosing between different products, weighing up the potential profitability of one technological option against another. The system therefore *closes off* numerous technical, economic and social possibilities, on a regular basis. It is easy to appreciate capitalism's overt destruction of productive resources which come about through crisis, bankruptcy and war; but there is another more insidious process at work whereby productive options are aborted before they ever come to fruition. This process is seen operating in a multitude of different areas. Potentially liberating new technologies are applied by corporations in the most deskilling, dehumanizing ways.[30] Potentially decentralized energy systems are reinterpreted by corporations in the most centralized, capital-intensive ways.[31] Potentially extensive Third World fuel resources are ignored by corporations for fear of giving Third World countries too much freedom for manoeuvre.[32] Capitalist economic development is characterized not only by what it *does* achieve, but also by the numerous productive options which it chooses to ignore or abort.

This leads to a rather different understanding of the 'obstacles' which capitalist social relations place on the development of the forces of production. Firstly, it emphasizes the issue of technological choice. Technological development, and human creativity, do not proceed down a single road. They seek to proceed down many roads – but capital, which seeks always to prioritize those options which appear profitable, continually sets up roadblocks. It is in *this* sense that capitalism acts as a fetter on the forces of production. It follows that a socialist mode of production would be characterized not by the more rapid development of capitalist technologies, but rather by the conscious adoption of quite *different* technologies, guided by quite different criteria. Proposals on the technological options which would be appropriate in Britain in moving towards a socialist energy strategy are made in the chapters which follow.

Secondly, the issue of technological choice immediately raises the question of who does the choosing, and this is not a separate or supplementary question. The 'forces of production' do not consist exclusively of machines, technology and raw materials – without the input of human labour these would be so many dead objects. The working class is therefore the primary force of production – and *its* development is also hindered and held back by capital. Each of the examples cited above illustrates the point: each of them shows capital seeking to divide, deskill and weaken the power of working people. Here again capitalism acts as a fetter on the development of the forces of production by crippling the self-development and self-determination of the working class.

The issue of technological choice is thus inseparable from the existence of independent workers' organizations and from the issues of workers' control and industrial democracy. These are the essential political conditions for socialism, and it should be clear that they are in no way distinct from the economic and technological conditions. Socialism implies a technological departure from capitalist priorities, a departure in the interests of working people, launched by working people. This can only occur in the context of new forms of collectivism and democracy in which workers are able to express their independent power. A socialist society, in other words, would be a much more actively *politicized* society than we know today. By definition, it would lack the motive force which drives capitalism: the constant search for profit, the constant drive for the self-expansion of capital. A viable socialist society would replace this with a different sort of motive force: the force of consciously chosen social priorities emerging from the constant ferment of debate and argument.

The central priority for a democratically planned socialist economy would be to reproduce and strengthen the conditions for democratic planning – just as the central drive under capitalism is to reproduce the conditions for capitalist growth and profitability. The necessary conditions for democratic planning are complex, including cultural and political factors as well as technological and material ones. However, one essential condition for the survival of a planned socialist economy would be for finite resources to be used as sparingly and efficiently as possible. Economic planning must to some extent subordinate today's demands to tomorrow's needs. Inefficient use of scarce resources today is an act of theft from future generations. It is a closing off of those future peoples' options and therefore a threat to their ability to continue with the development of a socialist civilization.

The immediate implication for energy policy is that the economy would, over time, move away from the capitalist trajectory of ever-expanding energy consumption and a steadily rising share of electricity in the energy balance. There would inevitably be a process of transition, during which time the infrastructure established under capitalism would be maintained and utilized: the structure of energy supply and use is too fundamental to social and economic life to be transformed all at once. Over time, however, the centre of gravity of the energy supply system would shift to prioritize conservation, to enforce depletion regimes for scarce energy resources, to ensure that the energy input for specific tasks was supplied in the most efficient and appropriate form, to phase out environmentally or socially unacceptable technologies, such as nuclear power, and to harness new benign sources such as the renewables.

Conclusions

The deliberate application and harnessing of social energy resources is fundamental to human activity, fundamental to that process whereby humanity progressively transforms its environment and therefore itself. Under capitalism, energy resources are exploited on an unprecedented and ever-expanding scale in the service of a blind and ultimately self-defeating drive for capitalist growth and profitability. In a non-capitalist country such as the USSR, historical circumstance has forced a pattern of development which duplicates the capitalist experience in many respects. Socialism, however, holds out the hope of striking in new directions, exploiting the full range of human ingenuity, choosing technical options on the basis of democratic planning and social need, and creating the basis for a politically and materially stable and sustainable society.

8. Forces for change

Faced with the prospect of an unsympathetic Tory government until at least 1987-8, what can socialists and/or energy activists do now to push for a change in energy policy? It is first of all important to realize the significance of the 'and/or'. There are many describing themselves as socialist for whom 'energy policy' is an also-ran. Yet socialism must, as a first principle, seek to ensure that people have sufficient food, sufficient warmth and adequate housing. All of these require energy and planned energy policies.

On the other hand, there are many working in energy campaigns who would not describe themselves as socialist. They may regard themselves as part of no movement or associated with the Green movement. As stated before, while one can sympathize with many Green ideas on energy policy, the view that society can live in perfect harmony with nature has serious shortcomings. It is the degree and form of disharmony that is crucial – the path forward must be a balance between socialist production for human need and ecological impact.

To move forward there must therefore be a closer co-operation between all who are concerned with the wellbeing of society, and indeed the wellbeing of the planet, and a drawing together of the various initiatives that have taken place.

Two major groupings have, through local and workplace organization, had a positive effect upon energy policy in this country in recent years: the labour movement and the anti-nuclear movement.

The labour movement

The NUM
Though this book was written before, during and after the 1984-5

miners' strike, it is not intended to analyse here the events surrounding the dispute. We shall rather look at the position of the NUM and analyse some of the lessons to be learn from the dispute.

That the coal mining industry has been in decline is not in question: in 1913, 1 million British miners produced 287 million tonnes of coal per year, over one-third for export. By 1959 production was at 200 million tonnes, produced by around 700,000 workers, and by 1978 it was down to 124 million tonnes produced by around 250,000 workers.[1] The reasons for this decline, as shown in Chapters 1 and 2, were political decisions which reduced the market for coal, to the benefit of other fuels, notably oil, gas and nuclear power.

The miners and, since its formation in 1945, the NUM, have always been regarded as the backbone of the labour movement. The historic struggles of 1972 and 1974 showed that, in a period of trade union militancy and low unemployment, the industrial muscle of the union could have a significant effect on the course of events in Britain. With these events still relatively fresh in their minds, it was inevitable that the Thatcher government, in its attempt to weaken and destroy the power of organized labour, would make the union a prime target for attack. The leaked Ridley report of 1978 confirmed that this was indeed part and parcel of the thinking of Thatcher's team (see p.83). Furthermore, if the full-scale introduction of nuclear power into this country were to be pursued, it would be necessary to weaken the power of the NUM. The leaked cabinet minutes of 1979 bear this out (see p.84).

There was a tendency by some, then, to see the 1984-5 dispute as a kind of final showdown: whoever lost would be defeated once and for all. It is certainly true that within the NUM itself divisions between the 'central' coalfields, such as Nottinghamshire, and those considered 'peripheral', such as South Wales or Scotland, were hardened. But these divisions were already in existence before the dispute started. They were hardened as a result of the introduction of the piece work scheme (see p.65). It is also true that support from other rank and file trade unionists was patchy and insufficient. While some unions, such as the NUR, ASLEF and the NUS, gave a good deal of support, others, such as the steel and power workers, failed to deliver. But in Thatcher's Britain of 1984, where self-interest and fear of unemployment were the order of the day, this too should have come as no surprise. Neither should the formation of the break-away union, the UDM.

However, to argue that as a result of the dispute the NUM is completely vanquished is both naive and short-sighted. The sup-port from all sections of the community, including the churches, the anti-nuclear groups, the peace and ecology movement, the black community, etc., together with the formation and con-tinuance of the support groups, in particular the womens' sup-port groups, shows that the miners' case was far from lost on the general public. The dispute undoubtedly raised a number of questions for the Left, such as the effectiveness of mass picket-ing, the manipulation of the media and the importance of broad alliances, but in answering these questions a mood of realism must prevail. This realism must take into account the prevailing political conditions, and the tactics of the dispute must be analysed in that context.

In the longer term there is no doubt that the NUM have a cru-cial role to play in any rational energy strategy. Coal will remain absolutely vital to British energy supply, particularly electricity, for many years to come, irrespective of the political persuasion of the government. The immediate tasks must be: to reunite the NUM around the issue of the future of the British coal industry; to encourage and develop the work already started by the union on the environmental issues connected with coal, such as its opposition to nuclear power and concern for cleaner coal-burn-ing devices; and to spread the case for coal among other workers, particularly those in the other energy industries. The NUM, far from being vanquished, is still a force for change within the labour movement.

Workers' plans

There have been a number of developments in recent years which represent the elements of a future alternative energy strategy arising out of the immediate problems and concerns of the working class.

The 'corporate plan'[2] developed at Lucas Aerospace in the

mid-1970s and other similar 'workers' plans' represent one such development. The Shop Stewards Combine Committee at Lucas succeeded in drawing together shop stewards from many different branches of the company's UK operations, thus encouraging a degree of united organization not possible in the 'traditional' trade union structures. The Combine Committee prepared the corporate plan as an alternative to redundancy and idle machinery. It proposed a range of 'alternative' products using existing skills and technology to produce socially useful goods such as a road-rail bus and kidney machines. In the energy field the plan included the development of heat pumps, solar fuel cell technology and a multiple-purpose power pack capable of adapting to a range of uses and designed with Third World production priorities in mind. The plan also incorporated energy saving into the production process itself and emphasized methods of work which enhanced creativity rather than implementing deskilling. Telechiric devices were notable in this area. Overall, the plan was drawn up not by a minority of radical design workers or outside academics, but by large numbers of workers involved in production at all levels from the shop floor to the design room.

The corporate plan could still become prominent again in inspiring future struggles against redundancy. Some of its ideas have, in fact, been taken up both by Lucas management and elsewhere and have proved to be both technically and commercially viable.

Lucas was not the only example of a 'workers' plan'. At Vickers, shop stewards drew up proposals for alternative products to replace tanks and armoured vehicles (at Vickers Elswick), and to replace warships (at British Shipbuilders Barrow naval yard). In both cases, as at Lucas, safe-energy technologies immediately presented themselves as socially useful alternatives to military hardware: solar power, wave power, tidal power and fluidized-bed coal-burning technology were among the developments suggested.

Within the power-engineering industry in the mid-1970s workers were also concerned about their future. Constant changes of mind on the nuclear programme, and an apparent hostility to the ordering of any further coal-fired power stations created considerable uncertainty. This had an immediate political dimension –

the crisis in the industry was exploited by Arnold Weinstock and his supporters in Westminster and Whitehall to call for a 'rationalization' of the industry under the aegis of GEC, the company he chaired.[3] Power-engineering workers in the north east then launched a successful campaign both to fight off GEC's takeover and to bring forward the ordering of the Drax 'B' coal-fired power station. This order, placed in 1977, was the first coal-fired power station ordered for 11 years. In the context of this continuing crisis, power engineering workers on Tyneside, at Parsons and Clarke-Chapman, produced their own workers' plans. Once again, for obvious reasons, energy-related products were given most prominence. At Parsons, CHP technology plus wind and wave power were proposed (see below). At Clarke-Chapman, these plus solar and tidal power, fluidized-bed technology and energy storage systems were put forward.

These initiatives – and this is by no means an exhaustive list – must be placed in context. First, they were the products of a specific period: a period of deepening recession and rising unemployment on the one hand, but also a period in which the Labour government in power was committed, on paper at least, to a 'radical' industrial strategy. The various workers' plans arose out of redundancy struggles, but they also arose because there seemed to be a possibility of support from the state.

Second, the workers' plans arose very much from the semi-official and unofficial structures of the trade union movement. The official co-ordinating body of the engineering unions, the CSEU, was positively hostile to the initiatives at Lucas and in the power-engineering industry. The workers' plans were, of course, a direct challenge to management prerogatives – an extension of collective bargaining to take in issues of planning and investment. But they were also a challenge to the official trade union leadership and their lack of official support was a source of political weakness in the plans.

The inspiration of workers' plans has been carried on through the work of the Centre for Alternative Industrial and Technological Systems (CAITS) based initially at the North East London Polytechnic and later the North London Polytechnic. CAITS has expanded the idea of workers' plans and has supported initiatives in many other companies including the Metal Box Company, Ford UK and International Computers. Much of the work has been related to energy issues but as the recession has deepened CAITS has inevitably been forced to take up the broader arguments of job losses and working time.

A similar venture was established in 1982 at Lancester Polytechnic, Coventry, entitled the Unit for the Development of Alternative Products (UDAP), again inspired by the Lucas workers' plans and again developing energy-related products such as windmills, heat pumps and Third World energy packs. Working with redundant British Aerospace workers, UDAP are investigating a wide range of socially useful products.

Workers' plans, to be successful, need a radical change of attitude by central government and trade unions. Without support for extensions of collective bargaining from both parties, or the backing of extensive industrial action, the plans will continue to be a solely defensive but largely impotent measure – their true value lying only in the demonstration of the potential available. Nevertheless, they represent a key element of a future socialist energy strategy and their continued development is a vital part of the process of its achievment.

Jobs from Warmth

One workers' plan is worth looking at in particular detail as it succeeded to a large degree in crossing the existing boundaries of the labour movement, and provides a pointer for future activity.

The Jobs from Warmth campaign to promote Combined Heat and Power/District Heating (CHP/DH) was initiated by the Joint Trade Union Committee at NEI Parsons as part of a plan for the power-engineering industry. In 1978, the shop stewards contacted a number of academic and other institutions including the Open University Energy Research Group, National Right to Fuel Campaign, Newcastle Energy Advice Unit, the District Heating Association and CHP consultants Orchard and Partners. Papers produced by these bodies were circulated to colleagues in the industry and a meeting was held with Newcastle City Council to persuade them of the validity of building a CHP/DH system for Newcastle and Tyneside. As a result, Newcastle was the first local authority to apply for status as a 'lead' city when the government set about a feasibility study into CHP/DH in 1979-80.

Thanks to the persistence of the Joint Trade Union Committee in not allowing the matter to rest there, other crucial events followed. Through lobbying the TUC and the Labour Party, and applying for funding from the Rowntree charitable trust, the Technology for Employment Project (TEP) was established in Newcastle in 1981. This body used the CHP/DH campaign as a base, looking for alternatives to unemployment in the north east, and produced a leaflet entitled 'Jobs from Warmth'[4] in June of 1981. The leaflet was widely distributed to many parts of the country and, as a result, the TEP was invited to speak at the annual conference of the Anti-Nuclear Campaign in September 1981.

This significant link with the anti-nuclear movement resulted in the formation of the national 'Jobs from Warmth' campaign with members actively campaigning for combined heat and power with their own local authorities. While these initially involved some of the government's nine lead cities – Edinburgh, Newcastle, Sheffield, Manchester and London – other areas such as Glasgow, and later Ipswich, also came in. The group existed from 1981 to 1983 and was successful in getting local authorities to take CHP/DH seriously in the face of severe government pressure on local government resources.

Local authority energy initiatives

Local authorities, whether Labour-controlled or not, have started to realize that energy issues are a vital part of their responsibility. In some cases, such as Tory-controlled Essex County Council, the move to save energy came about principally as a means of saving council money. Others, such as Newcastle City Council, were more concerned with questions of fuel poverty, bad housing and unemployment. Yet the progress to make authorities aware of the issues has been remarkably slow.

In autumn 1984, ten years after the first oil 'crisis', a report published by the Association for the Conservation of Energy[5] concluded that only 26 per cent of the 521 local authorities in Britain perceive it as part of their role to promote wise fuel use in the wider community; only 36 per cent have sought to implement energy plans for their own buildings; and just 20 per cent have carried out energy audits of their premises.

The reason often given for this lack of interest in energy and its use is a reluctance to pursue any options unless state finance is available. Nevertheless, where the more aware authorities have put ideas into practice the results have been shown to be worthwhile.

Amongst Conservative-controlled authorities, Essex County Council has led the way. Their commitment to energy conservation goes across the spectrum of services they provide: from courses arranged for building caretakers in how to get the maximum efficiency from boilers, to extra-curricular courses for primary and secondary schools, including in-service training for teachers, ranging from patterns of use in lighting to the assessment of heat loss through the fabric of buildings. While the primary aim of these efforts is to save council money, an inevitable spin-off is a greater awareness of energy conservation amongst council employees and clients.

In Labour-controlled Newcastle, on the other hand, the social benefits of conservation were very much the motivating factor. In 1983-4, alone, some £4 million was committed to insulation and heating measures.[6] Special priority is given to the needs of low-income households and the council is committed to continue the programme in all homes affected by ineffective heating and inadequate insulation. Tyneside is at the forefront in other areas. The £280 million metro train system was a move to improve fuel efficiency in local transport initiated by Tyne and Wear County Council and as outlined above, plans for a local CHP/DH scheme have been pursued jointly by Gateshead, Newcastle and Tyne and Wear Councils. Such a scheme would not only bring warmth to residents but would provide employment locally in the power-engineering, steel and construction industries.

Other authorities, such as the GLC, have also taken energy issues on board. The GLC-sponsored Greater London Enterprise Board has created LEEN – the London Energy and Employment Network – to save energy in London's houses, offices and factories and in so doing create jobs. LEEN works closely with tenants associations and academic institutions to provide an energy resource for Londoners.

These examples show that where local authorities take energy seriously much can be achieved. Unmet needs and wasted skills can be matched at a local level. The threat to these initiatives from public spending cuts, rate-capping and Metropolitan County abolition cannot be ignored, however, and it remains to be seen what long-term achievements will be made.

The anti-nuclear power movement

There has always been opposition to the nuclear programme in Britain but it was not until the 1970s that the anti-nuclear movement gained strength. Through the work of environmental groups such as Friends of the Earth and, later, specific organizations such as the Anti-Nuclear Campaign, the objectors became educated and informed of nuclear power and its implications. By the time of the Windscale Public Inquiry in 1977 demonstrations of over 20,000 people were possible and public sympathy was beginning to swing behind the objectors.

The shortcomings of the industry that had promised 'electricity too cheap to meter' and had delivered power stations renowned for their lateness and cost overruns, were obviously of major assistance to its opponents. After the accident at Three Mile Island in 1979 it seemed impossible to envisage a serious future for nuclear power in this country.

However the deliberate tactic by the Thatcher government of low-profile development has undoubtedly weakened the campaigns of those concerned with nuclear power. Nevertheless, a smaller, tighter network of activists has emerged and coupled with the growth of CND the movement has managed to maintain an effective voice.

Sustained opposition has led to a situation where it is now virtually impossible for the CEGB or other pro-nuclear agencies to attempt to develop a nuclear facility without widespread public opposition. At Portskewett, in Gwent, for example, the plans for a new nuclear power station were shelved after a protracted campaign; the test bore drillings in the Scottish Highlands were fought and won; at Luxullyan, in Cornwall, a prolonged occupation by local people of the site for a rumoured power station led to the CEGB's withdrawal of its plans; at Billingham, in Cleveland, opposition from local residents and politicians has forced the government to drop plans for a waste store; in Elstow, in Bedfordshire, a proposal for a shallow waste burial site was met with strong local opposition. Perhaps the most symbolic gesture was the declaration, in 1982, by Welsh local authorities of a 'nuclear-free' Wales.

In all of these actions opposition has been widespread across all political viewpoints and across all age groups and classes. The only exception to these successes in mobilizing public support would seem to be at Sizewell in Suffolk where the same degree of opposition was not encountered for the site of Britain's first proposed pressurized water reactor. There are several reasons for this, but perhaps the most telling are these: first, the CEGB already owned and operated a nuclear power station (a Magnox) at the site. Local people were therefore accustomed to the idea of such a potentially dangerous neighbour. Nearly all of the other sites mentioned above were 'green field' sites and were consequently that much less willing to play host to the development. Certainly the point has not been lost on the CEGB since of the five sites named to follow Sizewell 'B' (Hinkley Point, Winfrith, Dungeness, Sizewell 'C' and Druridge Bay), four already have a nuclear power station. It is significant too, that so far the most widespread opposition has been at the fifth – Druridge Bay.

Second, local authority opposition was virtually nil – one of the reasons quoted by the CEGB for their choice of site during the public inquiry. Suffolk County Council's virtual acceptance of the project was a major factor in the lack of weight in the campaign.

Third, the public inquiry into the proposal lasted over two years. This fact, and the level of detail discussed as a result, led to a lack of involvement from the local population. Given the government's refusal to fund objectors, the CEGB's placing of contracts for major parts for the reactor during the inquiry and various government pronouncements on the vital need for nuclear power over the period of the inquiry, it is hardly surprising that attendance at the event by the public rarely went into double figures.

Nevertheless, public opinion against nuclear power continues to grow[7] and while the CEGB and the government are still able to press ahead with their programme, progress has been slow and unsteady. The fact that opposition at the official level at the Sizewell Inquiry came from such 'establishment' bodies as the Council for the Protection of Rural England, the Royal Institute of British Architects and (while not objectors) even the Electricity Consumers' Council, is testimony to the degree of success of the whole anti-nuclear movement.

In analysing this success it is valuable to look at the work of two groups. One, Greenpeace, is well known and has featured in high profile in the movement. The other, PARTIZANS, while less well known, is important for other reasons. Both these groups have stepped out of the 'traditional' pressure group type of campaign in order to affect national events.

Greenpeace

Started early in the 1970s in Canada, Greenpeace has grown rapidly to an international organization which, as far as Britain is concerned, is now arguably better known and respected than other ecological organizations such as Friends of the Earth. Many of the early campaigns of Greenpeace centred on the plight of Canadian seals or the threat to whales, and the tactics of direct intervention between the hunters and the hunted via the use of inflatable boats attracted widespread publicity and admiration. It is perhaps this 'adventurous' willingness to put themselves into positions of danger for their beliefs that has earned Greenpeace respect even from its opponents.

With their emphasis on the ecology of the sea, it was inevitable that the organization would before long become embroiled in the arguments over nuclear waste dumping in the Atlantic. The crews of Greenpeace ships were soon putting themselves between nuclear waste barrels and the ocean. The effect that such action had can be gauged from the fact that recent designs for nuclear waste dumping ships have been modified to allow dumping from the hull of the ship rather than over the side.

However, action at sea was obviously not enough, despite the publicity and educational effect it was having, so work was started in another area. Greenpeace chose their targets well, centring on the one vital link in the chain – the National Union of Seamen (NUS) whose members were responsible for crewing the dumping ships. Throughout the late 1970s and early 1980s Greenpeace in the UK improved its relations with the union and lobbied its members well. This work, coupled with the action of Greenpeace groups internationally lobbying for and achieving a two-year moratorium on sea dumping by the ruling body, the London Dumping Convention, resulted in an almost unique situation whereby a trade union (the NUS) took a decision that the ecological damage caused by its members' employment was as important an issue as the members' pay and conditions. Despite Britain's preparedness to ignore the moratorium, and despite an offer of a considerable bonus, the NUS members refused to handle nuclear waste destined for dumping at sea. This decision has now been taken further to include railwaymen and dockers and resulted in no dumping taking place in 1983 or 1984. It also led to a combined TUC/government inquiry into sea dumping resulting in a complete ban in 1984, accepted by the Tory government, until 'all options for disposal are considered before dumping is resumed'.[8]

Greenpeace has continued its work in other areas, notably the reprocessing works at Sellafield (Windscale), bringing the public's attention to the long-term pollution of the Irish sea and surrounding beaches by the plant's radioactive discharges, and look likely to go forward with considerable public sympathy and support.

People against RTZ and subsidiaries (PARTIZANS)
In the summer of 1980 in South Dakota, USA, a gathering of people from 26 native nations and 30 other countries met to declare a united attack on multinationals 'which . . . through their economic and environmental domination, threaten our very survival'.[9] The British multinational, Rio Tinto Zinc, was targeted because of its nuclear activities and human/ecological record. Following a request from the Aboriginal people PARTIZANS was formed.

In May 1981 a week of action took place, co-ordinated by PARTIZANS and involving public meetings, films, pickets, etc. in 15 cities in Britain, Northern Ireland, West Germany, Spain, Portugal, New Zealand and Australia. These activities culminated in a tribunal held in London where RTZ 'victims' testified before a 'jury' made up of representatives from shareholding institutions such as the GLC, Guy's Hospital and Kent University. As a result of these and further actions some success was achieved in persuading British shareholders to disinvest with RTZ, e.g. the Salvation Army, NSPCC, the Bahai's and, sadly only one of the local authorities involved, Fife Regional Council.

Other tactics used by PARTIZANS to good effect include: the purchase of RTZ shares in order to attend their AGM and question publicly the policies of the company; the intervention in the yearly recruiting efforts of the nuclear industry at universities – the 'milk round' – in order to dissuade graduates from obtaining employment with companies such as RTZ; and, in conjunction with the Campaign Against the Namibian Uranium Contract (CANUC), the bringing of pressure to bear on trade unions responsible for members working in the transport of uranium from RTZ's notorious Rossing mine. This latter campaign has led, in part at least, to the CEGB's decision to cease obtaining its uranium from Rossing and to switch to Canada. Unfortunately the alternative is also owned by RTZ.

PARTIZANS' strength lies in their central theme of a concerted attack on a multinational company through the development of a campaign linking those native groups affected with activists in the First World, and tactics used to carry out that campaign. Their weakness has been their relative inability to attract active support for the campaign from the labour movement and elsewhere. PARTIZANS have, however, developed some important models for action.

The way forward

These then are some of the ways UK energy policy has been and continues to be challenged. In some cases, such as the anti-nuclear power lobby, the challenge is direct and immediate; some, such as the Lucas and Vickers plans, have arisen out of other struggles; some, such as the Greenpeace campaigns, spring from a concern for the environment and ecology. All are linked by a growing awareness that society must find democratic solutions to its energy problems which satisfy the basic human needs for warmth, power and light without destroying our planetary resources.

One crucial development in recent years has been a growing collaboration between concerned sections of the labour movement, such as the NUM, and the activists in the anti-nuclear movement. Indeed, the contribution of the anti-nuclear/pro-safe-energy movement to a general working-class intervention on energy issues has been a major one. Much critical work has been done in questioning the assumptions underlying energy practices over recent decades; and much practical work has been done to demonstrate the potential of conservation and of alternative and renewable energy technologies. The examples examined in Chapter 6 of the work of ERR, IIED, Elliot and NCAT show the levels of sophistication that this work has now reached.

If we add together the elements identified so far – the detail, inspiration and industrial relevance of the workers' plans; the strategic militancy of trade unions such as the NUM or NUS; and the creative contribution of the anti-nuclear movement – we have a significant combination of forces. These elements are scattered throughout the country, making it difficult to establish a geographical base from which to influence the local economy, but the initiatives of various Labour-controlled local councils may start to remedy this weakness.

Several Labour-controlled local authorities have developed ideas for reshaping the local economy, involving a degree of workers' control. Various problems have arisen here which require examination.

Popular planning
Underpinning the activities of the 'New Left' in local government lies the idea of popular planning. In theory, popular planning is a vision of nothing less than a transformation to a post-capitalist society, carried out by the activity of the working class through

union committees, community groups and local authorities, with the full support of a socialist government.

Central to popular planning is the principle that decisions relating to production and resources are not made according to the criteria of profitability. The role of a socialist government would be to provide the funding for the socialization of sections of the economy where workers' plans were sufficiently developed – so that the criteria of market competitiveness would be removed from product decisions.

At present it is obvious that the Labour Party is not following a course which makes these developments likely; neither is there currently sufficient national working-class support for such a development. Nevertheless, the vision is important and shows how popular planning and workers' plans might take on a greater significance in the future.

Problems have arisen when the vision of social transformation in the future becomes linked to the current operations of radical Labour local authorities. These authorities face a dual problem of insufficient funds or powers to carry out such programmes, and often insufficient commitment in the workplace and the community to such policies.

The net result, as has been seen with the GLC, is frequently of radical rhetoric linked to very ordinary and often unsuccessful interventions in the local economy. Where the GLC's Greater London Enterprise Board has intervened in disputes over redundancies the outcome on several occasions has been the establishment of co-ops or municipal enterprises employing a reduced workforce with no long-term protection against market forces.

The GLC's intentions are undoubtably highly commendable – funding is only given subject to the existence of certain rights and powers for the workers and unions, and an attempt is made via 'technology networks' to set up communications between the workplace, the community and sympathetic academic institutions in drawing up alternatives to redundancy. However, without a guaranteed buyer for their products (guaranteed either by state contracts or by demands placed as part of extended collective bargaining at other workplaces) these new enterprises are doomed in the longer run. In the meantime they necessarily function like any other businesses in the economy. The task of ensuring profitability by cutting wages or jobs, or by reducing the standards of working conditions, is left to the workers themselves. Far from a transition to socialism, initiatives such as these seem set to lead to either the transformation of workers into successful small businessmen/women, or the failure of the enterprise and the resulting demoralization of the workforce.

As if to stress this point, the areas where popular planning has been most successful have been in the public sector or in the field of planning. Projects such as 'The People's Plan for the Royal Docks' have, for example succeeded in involving all sections of the community and generally raising political awareness.[10]

Conclusions

There undoubtedly exists in Britain today all the potential for a significant change in UK energy policy direction from one of undirected greed and short-term interest to one of democratically planned provision for our long-term requirements. Despite obvious problems, the various sections of the labour movement are slowly beginning to come together with other individuals and groups with an interest in energy. Such a move is to be welcomed – and hastened.

Labour-controlled local authorities can provide the geographical base for bringing together the forces identified and for acting as a catalyst for tackling specific energy issues. These may take the form, for example, of a local CHP/DH scheme where the crucial arguments over the coming few years will be the financing, control and employment implications of the project. The input from trade unionists, energy campaigners, tenants' associations, local authority officers and members, etc, is essential if these functions are not to fall into the hands of private enterprise.

The technology for change exists and, through developments of the concept of workers' plans, could be made widely available.

The idea of popular planning is important, but a socialist approach to alternative plans at any level must ensure that the products are removed in some way from the pressure of the market and made subject to democratic planning for social need.

This ultimately requires either state intervention in funding and guaranteeing contracts, or an unprecedented extension of collective bargaining, for example, such that workers from one sector demand to work with products produced by particular workers in another.

A socialist approach to energy strategy incorporating all these elements is vital in that it can provide the framework for integrating all the diverse approaches in the labour and environmental movements and for focusing demands at a local and national level.

9. A socialist energy strategy

What, then, are the immediate steps that can be taken, to keep open the socialist option in Britain? More specifically, is it possible to identify the outlines of a radical energy strategy which could contribute to the wider task of socialist advance?

In 1981, the UK became a net energy exporter. This situation will last, on present trends, until some time in the 1990s. These two decades are therefore a unique opportunity for Britain, a breathing space during which strategic decisions must be taken which will determine the patterns of energy supply and consumption into the twenty-first century. The Tory government is using this breathing space to some effect in the name of private profitability and political advantage: as explained earlier (see p.94) it has encouraged the rapid exploitation of oil and gas, the expansion of nuclear power and a restructuring and privatization of coal. If this policy is pushed through, the UK will be forced to reenter world energy markets as a net *im*porter some time in the next 10-15 years, more vulnerable than ever before, having squandered its unique opportunity. Such vulnerability, in a sector as crucial as energy, would make it very difficult to pursue any sort of sustained socialist economic programme in this country.

A socialist economic strategy means removing an ever-widening range of economic activity from the dictat of profit so that production can increasingly be planned on the basis of social need, using the techniques of the social audit rather than the financial audit.[1] However, it makes all the difference in the world whether this 'planning', and this definition of 'social need', is carried out by state institutions claiming to act on behalf of the people, or by the independent organizations of working people themselves. The vast majority of the population in modern

Britain is working class and, as stressed earlier (see p.129), the working class is *the* primary force of production. Socialist advance can only be secure if the working class is taking increasing democratic control over production decisions, both as producer and consumer. A socialist economic programme must involve certain technical, legal and institutional steps, but it can only ultimately sustain itself if it simultaneously nurtures the political conditions for working-class power in society at large.

Nor is this mere rhetoric: working-class democracy and workers' control of production are not 'optional extras' in socialist development (see p.129). They are intrinsic to it, because socialism can only transcend capitalism by developing the forces of production in a quite new direction, a direction in which technological options are subordinated to social control; and this, in turn, can only take place if new democratic forms are developed by the working class to exercise that control. Any strategy which aims to move in a socialist direction must be based on a progressive expansion of working-class power in society.

It follows that the process of planning and preparing a socialist energy strategy is not something to wait for until a Labour government is elected to office. In fact it has already started in a wide range of working-class organizations: trade unions, Labour Party bodies, other political parties, local authorities, campaign groups, tenants' associations and so on (see Chapter 8). The task now is to piece together these many working-class energy initiatives into a solid political whole, a base upon which a coherent integrated energy programme can be built.

Legal and institutional measures will be necessary to carry out this task, but they will not be sufficient. It will be necessary also to tackle the politics of energy technology. To sidestep this issue would be to cut the ground from under the feet of the whole strategy. One of the characteristics of capitalist growth is the recurrent choice of technological options which consolidate capital's control and undermine working-class power (see p.128). A socialist energy strategy must be equally clear about choosing between which technologies are to be developed.

On the energy front, a serious strategy must mean choosing between available options while recognizing the economic, technical and political implications of these choices, and realizing that certain immediate political tasks are necessary to lay the groundwork. The strategy outlined in this chapter involves some hard choices for the labour movement. It means the reduced use of oil and gas, the abandonment of nuclear power, the expansion of coal and the development of conservation and renewables. Workers in the oil, gas and nuclear industries may well oppose the whole programme as being against their material interests. A political process therefore needs to be launched now to build contacts between workers in different energy sectors and create a common identity as 'energy workers'. Such contacts do exist in a formal sense at national level, in the TUC's Fuel and Power Industries Committee, but this purely bureaucratic liaison simply leads the committee to perform a careful balancing act, and in order to avoid antagonizing any party, it ends up by adopting the absurd policy of advocating expansion of *all* energy sectors at once (see p.72). Sensible progress can only be made once it is accepted that a socialist energy strategy must be based upon new industrial and technological priorities and that this must mean restructuring and redeployment in the energy industries. This case must be won not simply by discussions among trade union general secretaries, but by discussion between energy workers at local level, organized, perhaps, through regional TUCs or trades councils. Quite apart from its long-term strategic significance, the development of such contacts between workers would create a powerful trade union alliance: had such an alliance existed before the 1984-5 miners' strike, the outcome might have been very different.

Energy unions also need to link up with other organizations consumers (through tenants' organizations and community groups, as well as formal consumers' councils); local authorities (which will be central to many aspects of the overall strategy, including domestic insulation, improvement of the housing stock, conversion to coal-fired boilers, and local CHP/DH schemes); public sector trade unions (which organize the workers who will carry out local authority initiatives); and energy campaigners and researchers (such as anti-nuclear groups, environmentalist groups, and individuals in polytechnics or universities). The purpose of these links needs to be made clear. It is not simply a matter of holding meetings, producing documents and lobbying ministers. The aim should be to lay down appropriate energy plans at local level, identifying local problems and opportunities, analysing current patterns of energy supply and demand, spotting major areas of waste, establishing the age and life expectancy of the existing energy infrastructure, researching socially useful energy products which could be manufactured locally and generally starting the process of detailed popular planning for a socialist energy strategy. Without this local activity the national programme will never take off; and in the process of generating this activity, a new enthusiasm for grassroots democracy and a new recognition of the necessity of socialist planning may be born.

A socialist economic programme

Before looking in detail at the shape of a socialist energy strategy, a more detailed picture is required of the wider political and economic process of which it would form a part. It is assumed here that Britain will not experience a sudden revolutionary transformation, but that a majority Labour government could come to power and help to initiate a radical restructuring of society, if it supports and extends working-class power at home, and if it actively seeks a coherent network of progressive alliances abroad. In practice, this would mean the state taking an active role in defining and delimiting the scope of capitalist activity through nationalization, other forms of public intervention, planning agreements and, most importantly, through giving support to independent workers' initiatives.

Any socialist economic programme must tackle the question of energy as a major priority. Secure energy supply is fundamental to any human society, and above all to a highly complex and therefore very fragile industrial society. A clear outline for a socialist energy strategy is therefore essential to underpin the viability of socialist advance on a wider economic front. The central requirement is to move towards a stable and sustainable balance of national energy production and consumption, so as to avoid vulnerability to world market forces, and thus to improve the predictability, and therefore the 'plannability', of the energy sector itself. A functioning, democratically planned economy cannot be created by dictat. It must be constructed carefully, over time, from the materials at hand; but if basic energy supply cannot be predicted, then the most painstaking planning in other sectors will be in vain.

However, any new government taking office after the Tories will inherit a clutch of major, inescapable problems: 4-5 million unemployed, a decaying urban infrastructure, a much-reduced and badly lopsided manufacturing base, a battered or dismantled welfare state, and an economy uniquely vulnerable to the shifting moods of the capitalist world market. Any government seeking to tackle these problems must base its economic programme upon growth. However, growth is now an emotive term, and it is essential to be clear precisely what is meant by it.

The destructiveness and waste of capitalist growth is all too obvious, but this is growth of a particular kind: within capitalism, economic activity aims at increased profits, at an optimum rate of financial return on investment, and it is incidental whether the goods and services produced as a means to this end are socially useful or positively harmful. It is thus not only logical, but actually inevitable, that capitalist growth continues alongside rising unemployment and a rising wastage of human and material resources. Capital, with its constantly shifting production priorities, guided always by the pursuit of profit, is incapable of harnessing the full productive resources of society in a coherent, sustained and efficient way. In the UK, for instance, growth in recent years has centred on some industrial sectors (North Sea oil above all), but more importantly on the private services sector, especially financial services. These services are not genuinely productive or socially useful: they are essentially parasitic, relying for their existence on the present exploitative structure of the world economy. Clearly, a socialist economic programme would not be based on further growth of this sort. It would, instead, aim at growth in socially useful economic activity, based on popular planning and deliberately aimed at matching unused skills and resources with unmet social needs. The mechanisms whereby such a matching would take place would vary from one economic sector to another: in many sectors the market mechanism would still have to be tolerated.[2] In the energy sector, however, direct public intervention would be required.

It was argued earlier (see p.50) that the establishment of an energy-efficient regime requires investment: not just the patching up of the existing fabric of energy use, but the weaving of a new fabric. However, investment of this sort, and on this scale, is rarely logical for capital, either during recession or in boom conditions. New energy developments have always been pushed through by political pressure acting upon the market, not by the 'natural process' of market forces. The move towards an energy-efficient economy will be no different. It will certainly require a climate of economic growth and investment, but equally certainly it cannot count on the capitalist market to provide that investment.

The issue of fuel poverty illustrates the argument. Fuel poverty – the inability to pay for adequate domestic heating – affects hundreds of thousands of people in Britain. They experience it in terms of chronic discomfort, bad health, illness and, in some cases, death from hypothermia. This fuel poverty springs from material poverty, from low incomes, high energy prices, bad housing conditions, inadequate insulation and inappropriate heating systems. It cannot be tackled through the price mechanism of the market, because people who are unable to meet regular fuel bills are, by definition, unable to muster the capital resources which would be required to invest in a new heating system, proper insulation or a move to a new home. The only way to tackle fuel poverty is to step outside the warped logic of the marketplace and intervene directly by means of an externally funded programme of domestic insulation, appropriate heating systems and improvement of housing stock. This inevitably means economic growth in that it means an expansion of economic activity, a harnessing of currently unemployed resources. However, it is not capitalist growth – indeed, by capitalist criteria, an investment of this sort would be quite illogical. It is socially useful economic growth.

It is crucial that this distinction between capitalist growth and growth in socially useful economic activity, be made clear. If it isn't, then it is easy to fall into the trap of making a false choice between growth as such, and 'low growth' or 'zero growth'. This false choice leads on the one hand to utopian proposals from the Greens who reject growth altogether (see p.113), and on the other, to equally utopian proposals from certain elements in the labour movement which prioritize quantitative capitalist growth in a completely uncritical way (see p.63). Socialism certainly requires the expansion of economic activity, but the *quality* and *form* of that expansion is all-important.

For the UK, any attempt to expand socially useful economic activity must start from the recognition that the manufacturing industry has virtually collapsed in recent years, and the economy has drifted towards relying on a fragile, and largely parasitic, private-service sector and on the stopgap windfall of North Sea oil. Responsible growth must therefore entail a degree of reindustrialization.

However, it would be self-defeating to aim at anything like industrial autarchy. The aim, instead, should be to reestablish a manufacturing base around a range of socially useful and internationally tradeable manufactured goods, in place of the current reliance on the 'invisible' export of capital and private financial services.

Even a modest programme of industrial development would seem to imply high energy costs, however. Past experience suggests that industrial activity tends to become more energy-intensive as it advances. A socialist programme of reindustrialization therefore seems at odds with a socialist programme for energy efficiency. However, there is no fixed relationship between a given level of economic activity and a given level of primary energy consumption: it is all a question of the efficiency with which energy is used, and the priority which is given to maximizing that efficiency.[3]

If energy efficiency and long-term social need were established as industrial priorities, if they were built into the very structure of industrial investment and retooling, then the material and energy costs of industrial expansion would be kept to acceptable levels.[4]

A key component of this approach lies in the area of design.

Capitalist production, organized around the pursuit of profit, has developed a characteristic approach to product design based on 'planned obsolescence': products are deliberately designed for short lifetimes, so as to maintain product turnover, sales and therefore profits. While supremely irrational in terms of material and energy wastage, this strategy is perfectly 'rational' from capital's point of view. Products could, however, be designed for long life if a network of repair, renovation and recycling facilities were also made available. Not only would whole new sectors of employment be created in these activities, but the overall savings in raw materials and energy would be enormous. For instance, a car designed for a 20-year lifetime, rather than the current 8-10 years, would show a 72 per cent per car year energy saving over its lifetime.[5] If a programme of reindustrialization were pursued along these lines, emphasizing the intensive development of highly sophisticated, highly efficient new products and techniques, then the UK economy would benefit not only from the employment created and from the goods made available, but also from the export possibilities which would surely follow.

In several companies workers have produced alternative plans which identify socially useful products which their companies could produce with existing skills and resources, and which fit perfectly into this strategy (see p.134). These plans represent pointers to the range of socially useful products around which a carefully planned process of reindustrialization could take place. Such a process requires that both production decisions and markets are removed from the logic of profit.

So the question is, how can these new industrial priorities be enforced when private multinational capital continues to dominate industry in general and the energy sector in particular: in oil, power engineering, construction and so on. In dealing with these firms, a careful assessment of the balance of forces will be required. Nationalization will be needed for privatized firms such as Amersham International, Britoil, Enterprise Oil, the BGC and privately held parts of the coal industry. But nationalization should not be held up as a socialist panacea for all purposes. In industries with a global reach and a global market, nationalization may at best bring some limited defensive gains, and may at worst be irrelevant. In these instances it may be more effective in the short term to take a selective public stake, nationalizing sector leaders in order to exert pressure on other companies.[6] The oil industry is a case in point (see p.165).

The strategy outlined here clearly calls for a lot of money, involving significant investment not only in the energy sector itself but in an energy-efficient retooling of manufacturing industry. These financial costs must be balanced, however, against the costs of not pursuing this course: the costs involved in continued industrial decline, the destruction of coal reserves, the squandering of oil and the massively expensive construction of unwanted nuclear power stations. It is not intended here to put forward new or detailed financial proposals. Many of the essential components of a funding strategy, such as the reimposition of exchange controls, public control or ownership of the banks, and public direction over the investment strategies of financial institutions such as the pension funds, are already current in the socialist movement.

However, these measures leave many questions unanswered. Capitalism is a global system: not only do goods and services flow constantly from one country to another, but the conditions of economic activity in one country (costs of production, size of the national market, interest rates, etc.) interact with the conditions in others. A purely national strategy based on exchange controls, import controls and nationalization, is not enough, though all these measures are necessary parts of the overall approach. Secure socialist progress in Britain can only be achieved by building broad supportive international alliances.

There are two essential aspects to such alliances. First, socially useful economic growth cannot be sustained in Britain alone, and it has already been demonstrated that such growth is a prerequisite of the energy strategy outlined here. Such growth would necessarily be reflationary, and in the absence of parallel reflationary policies elsewhere it would run into some of the problems as the French 'dash for growth' in the early 1980s. Second, by embarking on a course of investment in a range of new technologies, Britain would lay itself open to massive import penetration by conventional products during the 'transitional period', before a new infrastructure had been laid down. It is quite clear that the UK could not establish anything like a siege economy – no country is more dependent on international trade. The emphasis must therefore be on finding ways of creating a network of alliances which would allow the national strategy to take root, and not be allowed to wither or be overwhelmed in its early days. This must mean, first and foremost, co-operation with socialist, communist and radical governments, local authorities and labour movements in Western Europe: the bulk of Britain's trade is with these countries and they do possess independent and influential socialist and labour movements. These alliances would be based on mutually supportive reflationary policies,[7] and on socially useful economic growth.

These partnerships would be further strengthened by a common interest in a planned, rational energy policy. Areas for collaboration are identified elsewhere (see below) – these would involve not only West European countries, but others as well. For instance, a working relationship with major oil producers, especially with OPEC, is essential, because the stabilization and restructuring of the world oil market would help not only Britain but also the oil-importing countries of the Third World.

Wider European links also need to be built. East European countries have experienced severe energy problems in recent years, due to an inefficient and dirty energy supply infrastructure, and to rising oil prices charged by the USSR. Trading contacts and joint projects in the development of energy-efficient equipment could be of mutual benefit to East European countries and to the UK and could contribute to a broader process of European détente and partnership.

Finally, to return to a point stressed earlier, this international strategy need not, and must not, wait until a sympathetic Labour government is installed at Westminster. International collaboration at governmental level will ultimately be necessary, but international collaboration at municipal and other levels is possible now and can help pave the way for governmental contacts later. The declaration of 'Nuclear Free Zones' by local authorities all over Europe opens the way not only to symbolic twinnings but to concrete co-operation on non-nuclear energy projects between authorities in different countries. Experience can be shared in areas such as insulation, the installation of solar collectors and heat pumps, and district heating schemes, as well as in energy-related issues such as urban architecture and public transport policy.

To sum up, a socialist economic programme must aim at an expansion in socially useful economic activity, and given the recent industrial decline of the UK, this must mean a process of selective reindustrialization. The energy sector itself would represent a sizeable portion of this industrial investment and would generate demand in other areas, such as steel and construction. While such a programme will inevitably have a certain energy cost, the technologies are available to keep this to an acceptable level, and it should be seen as an investment to establish the new infrastructure necessary for an energy-efficient economy in the long term.

This programme would not be an attempt to defend the 'consumer society' – though it would indeed improve the living standards of many working-class people. It would not be an attempt at Keynesian reflation – though it would indeed be reflationary. It would, instead, be an attempt at economic recovery based on a political and technical restructuring of the economy, and on a pattern of economic growth which aimed not at the multiplication of corporate profits but at the multiplication of socially useful goods and services.

A socialist energy strategy

The main aim of a socialist energy strategy would be to secure the energy sector as a socialist stronghold within the wider national economy. Without this key area, potential advances in all other sectors would be in jeopardy. However, such a strategy has certain implications:

(1) It means reducing the role of private capital in dictating patterns of supply and consumption. This implies energy conservation and efficiency so as to reduce reliance on capitalist suppliers of fuel or technology and to make patterns of energy use more predictable. It also means a deliberate policy of using domestic

energy resources, or those which can be supplied by politically reliable trading partners, rather than depending on resources supplied through the mechanism of the world market.

(2) It means working people – producers and consumers – constantly expanding their democratic control over the energy sector. This will only be possible with a stable, planned energy sector, one not subject to capitalist blackmail or sabotage. It also requires the development of technologies which lend themselves to democratic control rather than authoritarian hierarchies. The question of technological centralization is important here; it is also important to look at issues such as the labour process, environmental safety, security of fuel supplies, technological back-up, implications of accident or sabotage, and links with other industrial activities, whether socially useful or harmful (such as military production).

(3) Britain is, arguably, more integrated into the world capitalist economy than any other advanced capitalist country: isolationism or a 'socialist siege economy' are simply not available options. Any attempt at immediate delinking from the world economy would invite disastrous domestic and international repercussions. This is not to say that major steps in a socialist direction are impossible, but they must be taken with a full sense of the realities of world power, and with a conscious attempt to create a supportive network of alliances and partnerships between both governments and municipal authorities and workers' associations. Joint energy projects could provide a vital focus for these alliances (see p.159).

However, not all international contacts would be with supporters or sympathizers – trading links with purely commercial partners would need to be maintained as well. Though a socialist energy strategy would not in these cases be based on the notion of energy resources as market commodities, it might be necessary in order to defend the broader programme, to exploit the fact that they are widely regarded as such.

(4) Finally, to qualify the point above, any steps taken in Britain must be related to a clear understanding of global energy trends and problems, and should contribute to resolving those problems in a democratic, anti-capitalist way. If the UK were simply to

look after itself by seeking to take commercial advantage of the world energy market in order to finance an avowedly socialist economic programme, it would quickly undermine its own efforts. The strategy must be to exploit the structure of the capitalist market in order to create a widening international network of anti-capitalist practice.

In the sections which follow, there is no intention of setting out a 'future energy scenario', with detailed technical analysis and statistics: it has already been demonstrated (see p.59) that a wide range of energy options is open to the UK. The intention here is to argue politically for an energy strategy for Britain which is based neither on technocratic nor on utopian premises, but on a socialist commitment to working-class democracy and popular economic planning.

Conservation

Energy conservation underpins the whole strategy: it is essential if the sector is to be stable, predictable and susceptible to popular planning. It is also essential if the programme of selective reindustrialization is to be carried through without high energy costs. The crucial point, already stressed, is that conservation is not merely a patching-up job, but involves significant investment in new buildings, equipment and processes.

A major programme of insulation and investment in energy efficiency will affect all sectors of the economy: in the domestic sector, and in all buildings, there is enormous scope for the addition of insulation, and for any new building to be guided by tight, energy-saving regulations; in industry, as emphasized earlier, there should be installation of energy-efficient equipment and processes; in transport, major savings are possible from investment in an expanded public transport system and from the development of new vehicles. In the energy sector itself, the installation of new technologies, such as pressurized fluidized-bed combustion, CHP and renewables, should also be seen as effective conservation measures. However, it is important to be clear why we argue for these measures.

Advocates of energy conservation have pointed out that a public insulation programme could create a great many jobs, relatively cheaply. Insulation should not be seen merely as a cheap, low-wage energy option: labour-intensive, low-wage job creation is, after all, a key part of the Tories' economic strategy, and it would be ironic if socialists ended up arguing for an identical policy in the name of energy efficiency. A publicly funded conservation programme should pay proper wages and should be valued not because of its cheapness, but because it directly matches unused resources with unmet needs.

Many different areas for activity have been identified here, calling for different institutional arrangements. A domestic insulation and house building programme, while funded centrally, would be best carried out by local authorities using their own direct labour organizations and working closely with tenants' and residents' groups. Investment in energy-efficient industrial equipment and processes is far more complex, calling for effective control over industrial investment strategies and leading on to questions discussed elsewhere such as exchange controls, import controls, nationalization and planning agreements.

Coal
While energy conservation is vital, it does not rule out the need for new energy supply. Coal will be the key element in energy supply for the foreseeable future, both because of the size of UK reserves, and because of the many uses to which it can be put.

Trends over the last 20 years mean that coal is now overwhelmingly dependent on a single customer – the electricity supply industry. At the same time, its significance within that industry has been eroded by the construction of oil-fired and nuclear power stations in preference to new coal-fired plants, and by the closure of a large number of smaller coal-fired stations in the early 1980s. The immediate priority must therefore be to defend and extend the role of coal in electricity supply, in preference to oil and nuclear power. New power stations should be coal-fired, and this should be taken as an opportunity to improve both the cleanliness and efficiency of coal burning, with the introduction of pressurized fluidized-bed combustion, and CHP/DH.

In addition to this defence of coal's traditional market, new uses must also be developed. It has already been demonstrated that there is a large and expanding international trade in coal, and Western Europe is its main market. This is the obvious target for British coal exports as well – not only because of geographical and political links, or because of market trends, but also because high-quality British coals from Wales and Scotland could make a real contribution to the emerging 'clean coal' policy in Western Europe which has developed as a result of concern about acid rain. However, a sustained strategy of coal export would require investment in transport and loading and unloading facilities.

There are also new domestic markets for coal, in industry and in public and institutional buildings, many of which currently use oil-fired or gas-fired boilers for space and water heating and for process heat. There is a trend in private industry to convert to coal-fired boilers and this should be encouraged, together with more burning of British coal by the steel industry. It is estimated that a potential market for 27 million tonnes of coal per annum also exists in the public sector, in offices, flats, schools, hospitals and so on.[8] Local authorities could implement coal conversion programmes, as could other public sector bodies, such as the health authorities.

A clear policy is also required to deal with the recent expansion of opencast mining, which by the early 1980s accounted for about 13 per cent of all coal production.[9] Opencast mines are privately owned, often using non-union labour; where workers are unionized they are generally in the TGWU rather than the NUM. There is a clear need for opencast mining to be brought back into the publicly owned industry, and for opencast miners to be organized with other miners, whether inside the NUM or by means of a TGWU-NUM agreement.

There is no justification whatsoever for reducing the size of the coal industry – on the contrary, the available markets call for expansion. The NCB's strategy in recent years has been to invest in highly productive, highly automated 'superpits ' in the so-called 'central' coalfields, and to let pits in the 'peripheral' fields run down. The closure programme announced in March 1984, which sparked the 1984-5 strike, was only part of a longer-term plan to close down 'uneconomic' pits in the peripheral fields in order to make way for new 'low-cost' capacity as it comes on stream. The

NCB's use of the terms 'economic' and 'uneconomic' does not refer to the existence of reserves, nor to the social costs of closure, but merely to internal operating costs. Its closure programme implies that reserves will actually be destroyed, as shafts and tunnels collapse and flood.

A socialist programme for coal must be based on the proposition, defended by the NUM, that pits stay open until they become unworkable, whether as a result of exhaustion or of safety hazards. It must be based upon investment in the industry so as to exploit reserves to the full. It must be based on investment in new mining technology, not as a means of monitoring and controlling the workforce (which is the main purpose of the NCB's new MINOS computer system), but to improve working conditions.

However, a longer-term perspective is also required. The immediate task of defending and expanding the industry is vital in order to secure coal's role in electricity supply, export, industry and institutional heating. In the long term, however, it would be a criminal waste to use coal only for these purposes. First, electricity is the common carrier by which the energy of the renewables will be distributed: over time, renewables will therefore replace coal in electricity supply. Second, coal must be regarded not merely as a fuel for burning, but as a valuable and flexible hydrocarbon resource with multiple uses. Its use in power stations should be seen as a stopgap measure, before it really comes into its own.

The most obvious use of coal is as a substitute for the other, geologically rarer hydrocarbon fuels, oil and gas. Coal liquefaction (oil from coal) and coal gasification (gas from coal) are both technically feasible. The obstacles to their development are mainly financial, though South Africa has found it worthwhile to develop a large oil-from-coal facility which also produces other useful gases and chemicals as byproducts. Coal gasification can be used either to produce gas for power stations – a cleaner and more efficient alternative to coal itself; or to make synthetic natural gas to replace natural gas in the existing pipeline distribution network. Investment is needed in these technologies, tied into long-term depletion policies for domestic oil and gas

reserves. Perhaps less obvious than these uses, but just as important, coal could also be used directly or indirectly as a feedstock
for the petrochemicals industry.

In the short term and in the long term, coal should be central to
energy policy and industrial planning in Britain.

Oil

The flexibility, portability and thermal efficiency of oil, as well as
the existence of a global transport system largely dependent
upon it, mean that it will continue to be the premier internationally traded energy resource for years to come. The UK is fortunate in its oil reserves, in comparison with most other advanced
capitalist countries – all the more reason to value and protect
such reserves. Oil reserves left in the ground or under the sea are
not lost, but should be regarded as assets for the future.

The priority in oil policy should be to stop net exports, reduce
domestic consumption to the lowest possible level, and to reduce
domestic production to meet that (falling) level of consumption.
(In practice, both exports and imports will continue, as high-
quality light North Sea oil is traded for heavy crude, but the
emphasis should be on stopping *net* exports.) Oil consumption
has been falling in all economic sectors in recent years, except for
transport. It is in this area that oil conservation efforts should
therefore be concentrated by developing more efficient cars,
encouraging public transport over private, shifting passengers
and freight from road to rail where possible, and replacing diesel
locomotives with rail electrification. However, other measures
should not be ignored, such as the conversion of oil-fired boilers
to coal in industry and institutional buildings, and the conversion
of oil-fired power stations to coal.

There are several reasons why it is so important to reduce oil
consumption and protect reserves. First, it avoids the very real
danger of becoming a net oil importer again in the 1990s, at the
mercy of world market forces. Second, reduced UK oil exports
would have a significant effect on maintaining the world market
price of oil, which is itself essential to the commercial viability of
a high-cost production area like the North Sea. This would, in
turn, help to create the conditions for extended collaboration

with other oil-producing states, both inside and outside OPEC, in order to stabilize and restructure the world oil market.

In recent years, the main threat to the world oil price has come from the maverick behaviour of the North Sea producers, (Britain and Norway), and from Nigeria, whose own oil is comparable in quality to that of the North Sea, so that it feels constrained to follow the North Sea lead in pricing levels. If the North Sea producers were to work more closely with the OPEC countries and with other major oil producers such as Mexico and the USSR, it might be possible to stabilize the market and launch a political reorganization of it. For instance, a two-tier system might be envisaged, in which advanced capitalist countries continued to pay a market price, while oil-importing Third World countries were offered discount prices, discount plus trade credits, or barter deals. The UK is too small a producer to launch such initiatives independently – but it might achieve some influence among oil exporters generally if it showed itself to be committed to a genuine, long-term stabilization of the market.

Underlying this strategy is an assumption that oil-holding states, rather than private oil companies, are the long-term dominant force in the industry, not withstanding the recent impact of the spot market and short-term commercial trading on oil prices. This leads to the question of how to deal with oil companies operating in the North Sea and in onshore oil developments. The 1974-9 Labour government set up BNOC in 1976 and used it to take a public stake in all new oil developments from that date onwards, sharing the risks and the rewards with private companies. A socialist oil policy in the 1980s and 1990s will have to recognize the continuing dominance of private capital, given the structure of the world oil industry, but that need not mean selling out to Exxon, Mobil or Shell.

The task of oil exploration must be distinguished from oil production. In conducting exploration, which is a highly risky business, the big oil companies are no better equipped in terms of expertise, technology or capital resources than many smaller companies. It would therefore be quite feasible to contract either large or small exploration companies to search for oil, allowing them to take the risk and giving tax or other concessions if they are successful. Alternatively, a new public exploration company could be set up. Once reserves are identified, there need be no hurry to move to large-scale production, given that overall policy would be to hold production down – although the large oil companies will be eager to move to production because that is where profits are to be made. It is precisely at this point that the host state is therefore in a position to dictate terms, and to enforce its long-term depletion policy. The strategy for the North Sea should not therefore be one of crude nationalization, but of exploiting the structure of the capitalist market for non-capitalist purposes. However, a direct public stake in the North Sea will be a necessary part of the strategy: at the very least it would involve renationalization of Britoil and Enterprise Oil, and it should also involve far more effective control over BP.

Perhaps the main argument against reduced production of North Sea (and onshore) oil is that it would lead to reduced oil tax revenues, and therefore to higher income tax and/or higher public borrowing. Oil revenues have indeed been substantial in recent years, providing up to 14 per cent of the government's total tax income. But North Sea production is already at or past its peak, and revenues will inevitably decline in the next few years. The Tories have already squandered the best of Britain's oil. The task now is to enforce a depletion policy for those reserves which remain, and to prioritize the long-term economic benefits of oil self-sufficiency over the short-term pursuit of immediate tax revenues.

Gas

Natural gas, like oil, is a valuable fuel and extremely efficient at certain energy tasks. However, compared to coal, domestic resources are limited. If consumption and production trends continue as at present, there is a good chance of major gas imports in the 1990s.

As with oil, policy should concentrate on reducing gas consumption to those tasks where it is clearly the most appropriate fuel – especially small-scale heating where fine tuning is required. Over the past 15 years, gas consumption has expanded in all areas of the economy, including bulk heating in industry and in the institutional/commercial sector. This is quite absurd, given the relative balance of coal and gas reserves. The commitment to expand the use of coal (see pp. 000) is clearly also a commitment to conserve natural gas, whether by converting of gas-fired boilers to coal, or by replacing of gas-fired central heating by coal-fired CHP/DH schemes.

Although the immediate emphasis should be upon conserving gas reserves, the medium-term effort should focus on finding substitutes. The prospect of coal gasification was discussed earlier; biomass is another potential source of synthetic natural gas. In addition to these technical developments, there is always the option of gas imports – the international trade in gas is growing steadily. The most obvious sources would be the USSR, whose gas could be imported by a pipeline link to Western Europe, or perhaps Algeria, which would supply liquefied natural gas (LNG) by tanker. In both cases there are environmental or safety hazards to consider. Soviet gas development is causing catastrophic damage to the delicate ecology of Western Siberia, while LNG transport is extremely dangerous, being at constant risk from major explosions. All these issues need weighing up.

At the time of writing it appears that the Tory government intends to privatize the British Gas Corporation (BGC) during the 1985-6 parliamentary session. Obviously a socialist energy strategy would mean taking it back into public ownership, and since the Tories seem set to sell it off as a single body, this should present no major problems. Future gas exploration and production activities should be planned in collaboration with those for North Sea oil (see p.165); it may indeed be sensible to set up a single public body to co-ordinate the exploration and production of all mineral resources on the continental shelf.

Nuclear power
The analysis of the nuclear industry presented earlier (see p.25) leads to certain, very clear conclusions. Nuclear power is incompatible with a socialist energy strategy and an attempt to move towards a socialist society. This incompatibility springs from certain very basic, material aspects of nuclear technology itself.

First, both conventional fission and fast reactors consume and generate materials which can remain toxic and radioactive for hundreds of thousands of years, posing environmental hazards on a timescale which rules out any guarantee of a sustained and adequate response by human society. In the face of these unprecedented dangers, pro-nuclear advocates can only fall back onto a faith that 'scientific progress' will somehow, eventually come up with a solution. But a socialist and materialist approach is based not on a belief in abstract 'scientific progress', but on a truly scientific analysis of the real movement of human society, which must include a clear sense of the delicate relationship between human society and the natural environment. Although that relationship is dynamic, although humans act upon the environment and transform it, science teaches that there are necessarily ecological limits to that activity. Human ingenuity consists precisely in recognizing those limits and exercising itself creatively within them. To develop nuclear power, with all its attendant hazards, is to deny the ecological context of human existence and to forget the brief timescale of human institutions – it is a profoundly unscientific, wilfully ignorant undertaking, incompatible with human security and progress, and incompatible therefore with socialism.

Second, the development of nuclear power has historically been inseparable from the development of nuclear weapons, and now the international proliferation of nuclear power is providing the technological base for the parallel proliferation of nuclear weapons. To continue to develop nuclear power is to contribute to the continued spread of nuclear weapons and to the growing likelihood of nuclear war somewhere in the world.

Third, for all the reasons outlined above, the nuclear industry must inevitably be hedged around with security restrictions and safety precautions which can only serve to fragment the workforce and to prevent the emergence of an independent and united workers' voice. As long as the existence of nuclear facilities is accepted, then there is a possibility of nuclear accident or nuclear war, and the consequences of this for human society would be so catastrophic that a tight preventative security regime must be maintained, involving restrictions upon both workers and ordinary citizens. Nuclear power is incompatible with basic democracy, let alone socialism.

Fourth, nuclear power is being developed not because it is needed to meet energy needs, but because a number of major corporations in the advanced capitalist countries have already invested heavily in the technology, encouraged by their domestic state powers, and are now desperate to maintain a return on this investment. It has already been demonstrated that the British nuclear programme has more to do with corporate profitability than with energy needs (see p.41).

Finally, as if to demonstrate the specific manifestation of all these general points, nuclear power is being developed in Britain, in the 1980s, as part of a quite explicit political strategy. The leaked Tory Cabinet minutes of 1979 (see p.84) make it quite clear that nuclear power is intended to replace coal in electricity generation and to help inflict a strategic defeat on the labour movement in general, and the NUM and transport workers in particular.

It follows that a socialist energy strategy would aim to phase out nuclear power as rapidly as possible, recognizing that it is not only unnecessary in energy terms, but undesirable on many other counts as well. This must mean first and foremost a commitment to close down, or halt the construction of, nuclear power stations, though the speed of this process is a matter for debate (see p.177 below). The nuclear industry also comprises installations other than power stations, including facilities for research, fuel enrichment, fuel fabrication and reprocessing. These do not merely service existing conventional fission reactors, they are also associated with the fast reactor and with the nuclear weapons programme. The phasing out of nuclear power generation must therefore be associated with a parallel withdrawal from fast reactor development and with a programme of nuclear disarmament. In fact, nuclear disarmament cannot be effectively carried through without the simultaneous closure of so-called 'civil' nuclear facilities. If they continue to exist, the option of nuclear rearmament is always open and the political impact of the initial disarmament programme would be lost.

This programme of nuclear shutdown obviously implies the

abandonment of enormous material resources and the writing off of decades of capital investment. On these grounds alone it might appear extravagant or wasteful. However, the real wastage has already been incurred in the historical process of launching, and then sustaining, a massive programme of investment in a disastrous technology. The choice today is between continuing to pour scarce resources into a nuclear programme which is socially, politically, environmentally and militarily undesirable; or cutting society's losses and getting out.

The jobs implications of a nuclear closure programme would have to be carefully studied. Some power station workers currently employed at nuclear stations could be redeployed to new, smaller coal-fired CHP stations. Many workers at the heart of the nuclear industry – at sites such as Sellafield, Springfields, Harwell, Aldermaston and Capenhurst – could apply themselves to the pressing problems of decommissioning nuclear power stations and of devising the safest possible long-term disposal of those radioactive wastes which have already been accumulated. Nor would the abandonment of nuclear power damage those industries which are currently associated with it – power engineering and construction. On the contrary, a steady ordering programme for modern coal-fired power stations would be far preferable for these industries to the current situation of sporadic and unpredictable nuclear orders.

Abandonment of nuclear power is not even a particularly radical move. Several other advanced capitalist countries are running down or scrapping previously ambitious nuclear programmes, either as a result of referendum decisions (Austria, Sweden, Switzerland) or of market and political pressures (USA).

Finally, it is important to identify the international implications of a British abandonment of nuclear power. The current state of the world nuclear market is weak. Many countries which were previously nuclear enthusiasts are now withdrawing or proceeding very cautiously; nuclear corporations are plagued with chronic overcapacity; there is too much uranium chasing too few customers; the economics of reprocessing and the fast reactor look increasingly absurd; and fusion is getting nowhere. However, within this vulnerable world market the UK occupies an important position. Its projected PWR programme is of immediate commercial importance to the world's leading nuclear corporation, Westinghouse, which will be the main supplier – but it is also of symbolic importance to the world industry as a whole, representing a much-needed vote of confidence. Britain is also involved in the URENCO uranium enrichment consortium; runs one of only two commercial reprocessing facilities in the world; is an important partner in the West European fast reactor project; and hosts the EEC fusion project. Withdrawal by the UK from all these areas would send shock waves through the nuclear industry, deepen its malaise and encourage other waverers to withdraw as well.

Stopping the PWR programme is clearly the most immediate priority. This would involve breaking the complex network of alliances between private capital (Westinghouse, GEC and other companies in the National Nuclear Corporation) and state bodies (CEGB, Department of Energy and the Treasury). It must also mean breaking with the TUC-Labour Party tradition of support for a 'British' nuclear reactor. Nothing will have been gained if the PWR is scrapped only to be replaced by a revamped AGR programme. The PWR is unacceptable not because it represents American technology, but much more importantly, because it represents nuclear technology.

Withdrawal from the whole area of reprocessing and the fast reactor is also important, and this too would have a major international impact. Both are already under pressure. If Britain pulled out of the West European fast reactor project, the overwhelming burden of that project would revert to France. France is highly committed to nuclear power, but the sheer scale of its programme has already bankrupted large parts of its electricity supply and power-engineering industries. If UK withdrawal from the fast reactor project were to be coupled with proposals for joint work in other energy technologies, it might at least encourage a reduction in the present wholeheartedly nuclear French energy strategy. In reprocessing, it would be counterproductive for the UK to suddenly refuse to accept any further foreign nuclear wastes: this would simply create a new problem of waste storage in other countries, in a way which would be construed by those countries as highly provocative and hostile. A negotiated settlement would be required in which a clear closure date for the Sellafield complex would be set, and which would be tied to proposals for future close collaboration in other, non-nuclear energy fields. Once again, the whole strategy would need to be mapped out with French intentions very much in mind: the French plant at Cap La Hague is the only other commercial oxide reprocessing facility on the international market.

The role of the state in the British nuclear programme continues to be highly significant – so that the programme cannot be expected simply to collapse under unfavourable domestic market conditions, as has happened in the USA. At the same time, however, multinational capital is tending to develop a nuclear market at a world level, beyond the reach of individual states. Between these two components – a continuing state role and the development of an international market – there is a certain tension, but they are ultimately complementary rather than contradictory. This means that political action which leads the British state to withdraw from nuclear technology can have international market ramifications and contribute to the slow collapse of the industry at a world level. In particular, it will hit at the US nuclear corporations which are seeking to dominate the British market and at the emergence of joint West European nuclear initiatives. However, UK nuclear withdrawal will only have this benign impact if it is planned and phased, so as to recognize the energy constraints on other countries, and so as to work with them in developing joint non-nuclear energy projects.

Renewables

The histories of both oil and nuclear-power industries demonstrate that there is nothing 'natural' about the emergence of new energy technologies: in both cases the necessary political and market conditions had to be created, not only by the actions of private companies, but also by their respective domestic states. It will be no different with the renewables. Energy markets as they exist now are structured too firmly around established technologies for the renewables to be adopted on a large scale. Individual companies may favour their commercial development on a small scale, but if the renewables are to be fully developed it will only be as a result of a political commitment backed by public money and public policy.

The potential contribution of renewable energy sources in the UK has been made clear earlier. It is important that these many different technologies are not lumped crudely together. Priorities must be identified. The immediate priority for the UK is to develop those renewables which can supply electricity on a significant scale, so as to be introduced in place of nuclear power stations and so on, in the early twenty-first century, to replace coal in electricity generation, thus freeing coal to be used as a feedstock for substitute oil and gas fuels. The sources which spring to mind in this context – wave power, wind power and tidal power – are also those on which most research and development work has been done (which is not to say that it has by any means been adequate).

Of the three, wind power has been the most favoured, with both private capital (the Wind Energy Group and Howden) and the CEGB pursuing it. Two serious proposals for a tidal barrage on the Severn estuary have also been advanced: the smaller project is to be preferred on environmental grounds, but electricity could be generated from many other tidal sites besides the Severn. Finally, wave power has the greatest ultimate energy potential of all, but has also suffered the most severe cuts in government funding. The UK's wave-power potential should be seen as a natural asset, comparable in nature and greater in long-term significance than the country's offshore oil reserves, and it should be receiving investment on an appropriate level.

Wind, wave and tidal power are therefore the three renewable technologies which should be receiving priority as part of an integrated socialist energy strategy. However, the drawback of these and of certain other renewable sources, often pointed out by critics, is that they provide energy only on an intermittent basis. Clearly the electricity supply system could not be built around direct input from intermittent sources: the whole value of the national grid is that it provides adequate electricity to the customer on demand. The development of the renewables must therefore be associated with the development of energy storage technologies. Many options are available: pumped storage schemes, pressurized air, flywheels and batteries are all possibilities, at varying stages of development. Clearly there is a great advantage in an electricity supply system based on energy storage, as compared to the present system which is based simply on gross overcapacity: many power stations stand unused for most of the year, coming on stream only to top up the grid at times of peak demand, representing an enormous waste of resources, capital and capacity.

While the development of renewables geared to public electricity supply should be a priority, other, smaller-scale technologies, such as solar collectors and heat pumps, could be installed on a wider scale. The obvious context for these would be as part of a national programme for insulating and improving the housing stock, through the local authorities.

Ultimately, however, the development of renewable technologies cannot be pursued on a narrow national basis. It must be seen as an international collaborative effort, complementary to UK withdrawal from its current international nuclear agreements. Many other countries have experience of the renewables upon which Britain would want to draw and to which it could usefully contribute: wind power (Denmark, USA); wave power (Norway); solar power (Japan, USA); geothermal power (Nicaragua); tidal power (China, France, USSR); biomass (Brazil, France). Furthermore, many Third World countries which cannot afford to launch their own research would stand to benefit from international development programmes, especially in the areas of solar energy and biomass.

Electricity supply

Many of the proposals advanced here touch on the electricity supply system. Electricity is an important form of energy, absolutely necessary for some purposes, but it needs to be put into perspective. Electricity supply currently consumes about 35 per cent of primary energy in the UK and delivers about 13 per cent of the energy actually received by final users. It has been estimated that only about 8-9 per cent of end-use energy needs to be delivered as electricity.[10,11] But this 4-5 per cent difference in electricity supplied represents perhaps a 12 per cent difference in *primary* energy consumption, because of the energy costs of generating electricity. It has already been argued (see p.122) that capitalism favours the delivery of energy in a flexible form such as electricity, because this provides it with a wide range of technical and marketing options; and that this inevitably leads to electricity being used for many inappropriate purposes. A socialist energy strategy would not develop electricity for its own sake, but would seek to find the optimum level of electricity supply in the economy, given its specific characteristics as a delivered fuel.

The immediate implication is that the electricity supply system could be considerably reduced in size. First, it could be reduced by withdrawing electricity from those markets for which it is ill suited, and by substituting more appropriate energy sources plus conservation. Second, it could be reduced by cutting back on the excessive planning margin currently used by the generating boards. This planning margin – the margin of installed capacity over and above peak demand – is currently 28 per cent. Until the late 1970s it was 20 per cent, and it has been estimated that the extra 8 per cent has cost £6 billion in largely redundant plant.[12] However, this technically redundant plant proved itself to be politically invaluable for the Tories in 1984. The existence of large reserve capacity, and more specifically oil-fired reserve capacity, was an essential asset to the government during the 1984-5 miners' strike.

If the problem is approached from a different direction, however, by asking the question, 'How much electricity does Britain *need*?' then radical changes are clearly seen as possible. Assuming that total energy demand remains constant for the foreseeable future (a generous assumption, given that it fell by 12 per cent in the period 1974-84), that as much as 10 per cent of end-use energy needs to be delivered as electricity, and that a 20 per cent planning margin is sufficient in the electricity supply network, then approximately 25 per cent of present generating capacity could in theory be scrapped. This could obviously not be done overnight. But it would be possible to close all nuclear power stations down by the early 1990s, so long as new capacity started to come on stream from the mid-1990s. Initially, this new capacity would consist of small to medium-sized coal-fired CHP stations in major cities. Around the year 2000, a number of large power stations may be due to retire (Fawley, Longannet, Pembroke, Ratcliffe), and large-scale input would be required to replace these – but by this time, contributions could be expected from renewable sources, most probably from wind-power schemes and from a Severn barrage.

This programme is obviously speculative. It may be necessary to phase the nuclear rundown over a longer period of time, or to put back the retirement dates of other power stations. The important point is that, within the context of a planned energy policy, there is enormous scope for restructuring and making more efficient the electricity supply system. Although the system would be operating with less capacity, there would be a net beneficial effect on the industry. Power engineering would have a steady and predictable pattern of orders, rather than the recent boom and bust experience; and enormous capital resources currently tied up in maintaining superfluous generating capacity would be released for useful investment elsewhere.

Summary

□ A planned energy strategy, aimed at the appropriate and efficient use of energy resources, is an essential component of any socialist progress in Britain;
□ After seven or eight years of Tory rule, drastic measures will be necessary to undo the damage done to coal, the squandering of oil and gas, the neglect of conservation and the renewables, and the sinister lease of life given to nuclear power.
□ Only the labour movement, together with other radical forces, is capable of undoing this damage and setting the scene for a sane and sustainable energy policy into the twenty-first century, as part of a wider programme of socially useful economic growth. Much can be done immediately, but the return of a Labour government responsive to these forces is also essential.
□ Time is short. If there is no change by the early to mid-1990s,

the UK may find itself irrevocably committed to dependence on world energy markets, to nuclear power and to domination by multinational capital for the foreseeable future.

Notes

Introduction

1. Malcolm Wicks, 'Cold Conditions: Hypothermia and Health', in Jonathan Bradshaw and Toby Harris (eds.), *Energy and Social Policy*, London: Routledge & Kegan Paul, 1983, p. 89.
2. *Ibid.*, p. 94.
3. Pete Wilkinson, 'Nuclear Waste, Transport and Sizewell' *New Ground*, No. 4, Winter 1984, Journal of SERA, p. 12.
4. Dave Elliot, 'The Future of Coal', *New Ground*, No. 3, Autumn 1984, Journal of SERA, p. 11.

1. World energy trends

1. G.F. Ray, 'Europe's Fairwell to Full Employment', in Daniel Yergin and Martin Hillenbrand (eds.), *Global Insecurity*, Harmondsworth: Penguin, 1983, p. 201.
2. Joji Watanuki, 'Japanese Society and the Limits to Growth', in Yergin and Hillenbrand, *op. cit.* p. 169.
3. Robert Dohner, 'The Bedevilled Amerian Economy', in Yergin and Hillenbrand, *op. cit.* p. 69.
4. Joji Watanuki, *op. cit.*, p. 179.
5. *Financial Times*, 5 December 1983.
6. Robert Dohner, *op. cit.*, p. 69; Richard Barnet, *The Lean Years*, London: Sphere, 1981, p. 49.
7. Ian Smart, 'Energy and the Power of Nations', in Yergin and Hillenbrand, *op. cit.*, p. 363.
8. Jim Falk, *Global Fission*, Melbourne: Oxford University Press, 1982, p. 112.
9. *New Scientist*, 21 March 1985.
10. Gerald Foley, *The Energy Question*, Harmondsworth: Penguin, 1981, p. 112.

11. Daniel Yergin, 'Crisis and Adjustment: an Overview', in Yergin and Hillenbrand, *op. cit*. p. 8.

12. Richard J. Barnet, *The Lean Years*, London: Sphere, 1981, p. 77.

13. Gerald Foley, *op. cit.*, p. 140.

14. G.F. Ray, *op. cit.*, p. 202.

15. Martin Ince, *Energy Policy*, London: Junction, 1982, p. 39.

16. Robert Dohner, 'The Bedevilled American Economy', in Yergin and Hillenbrand, *op. cit.*, p. 69.

17. Jean Sain-Geours, 'The Social Contract Under Stress in Western Europe', in Yergin and Hillenbrand, *op cit.*, p. 263.

18. Daniel Yergin, 'Crisis and Adjustment', in Yergin and Hillenbrand, *op. cit.*, p. 11.

19. Peter R. Odell, *Oil and World Power*, 6th edition, Harmondsworth: Penguin, 1981, p. 55.

20. *Financial Times*, 4 November 1982.

21. Gerald Foley, *op. cit.*, p. 113.

22. Althea L. Duersten and Arpad von Lazar, 'The Global Poor', in Yergin and Hillenbrand, *op. cit.*, p. 274.

23. *Ibid*.

24. Thijs de la Court *et al.*, *The Nuclear Fix*, Amsterdam: World Information Service on Energy, 1982, pp. 145-50.

25. United Nations Environment Programme, 'Hydro-power', in Robin Clarke (ed.), *More Than Enough?*, Paris: UNESCO, 1982, p. 104.

26. Andrew Mackillop, *Energy and World Development*, Edinburgh: Scottish Education and Action for Development, 1981, p. 3.

27. Amory B. Lovins, *World Energy Strategies*, New York: Harper & Row, 1980, p. 18.

28. Erik P. Eckholm, *Down to Earth*, London: Pluto, 1982, p. 22.

29. *Ibid.*, pp. 136-7.

30. *Ibid.*, p. 156.

31. *Ibid.*, p. 172.

2. British energy policy and the world market

1. Michael Tanzer, *The Energy Crisis*, New York and London: Monthly Review Press, 1974, p. 48.

2. Bizhan Jazani, *Capitalism and Revolution in Iran*, London: Zed Press, 1980, p. 27.

3. Michael Tanzer, *op. cit.*, p. 51.

4. Philip Armstrong *et al.*, *Capitalism Since World War II*, London: Fontana, 1984, Chapter 5.

5. Richard J. Barnet, *The Lean Years*, London: Sphere, 1980, p. 50.
6. Michael Tanzer, *op. cit.*, p. 18.
7. Mohssen Massarrat, 'Oil the dollar and nuclear power', *Race and Class*, Vol. XXII, No. 4., Spring 1981, pp. 354-5.
8. Tony Hall, *King Coal*, Harmondsworth: Penguin, 1981, pp. 29-30.
9. *Ibid.*, p. 30.
10. HMSO, *Digest of United Kingdom Energy Statistics 1983*, London: HMSO, 1983, Fig. 2.
11. Gerald Foley, *The Energy Question*, Harmondsworth: Penguin, 1981, Table 3.
12. Philip Armstrong *et al.*, *op. cit.*, p. 313.
13. Mohssen Massarrat, 'The energy crisis: the struggle for redistribution of surplus profit from oil', in Petter Nore and Terisa Turner (eds.), *Oil and Class Struggle*, London: Zed Press, 1980.
14. HMSO, *Digest of United Kingdom Energy Statistics 1983*, Fig 2.
15. *Financial Times*, 5 December 1983.
16. Daniel Yergin, 'Crisis and adjustment: an overview', in Daniel Yergin and Martin Hillenbrand (eds.), *Global Insecurity*, Harmondsworth: Penguin, 1983.
17. *Financial Times*, 3 March 1984.
18. *Financial Times*, 11 August 1984.
19. See e.g. Walter C. Patterson, *Nuclear Power*, 2nd Edition, Harmondsworth: Penguin, 1983.
20. Brian Jenkins and Gunter Minnerup, *Citizens and Comrades*, London: Pluto, 1984, p. 120.
21. Peter Pringle and James Spigelman, *The Nuclear Barons*, London: Sphere, 1983, p. 75.
22. Kelvin Spencer, in *Sizewell Reactions*, 13 December 1983.
23. William Cannell and Renee Chudleigh, *The PWR Decision*, London: Friends of the Earth, 1984, p. 31.
24. Sheila Durie and Rob Edwards, *Fuelling the Nuclear Arms Race*, London: Pluto, 1982, p. 20.
25. Martin Spence, 'Exporting the "Peaceful Atom"', in *No Clear Reason*, Radical Science 14, London: Free Association Books, 1984, pp. 82-4.
26. William Cannell and Renee Chudleigh, *op. cit.*, p. 35.
27. Peter Pringle and James Spigelman, *op. cit.*, pp. 161-4.
28. William Cannell and Renee Chudleigh, *op. cit.*, p. 40.
29. Martin Spence, 'Nuclear Capital', *Capital and Class*, No. 16, Spring 1982, pp. 9-10.
30. Czech Conroy, *Rethink Electric*, London: Friends of the Earth, 1979, p. 3.

31. The *Journal* (Newcastle Upon Tyne), 8 January 1980.
32. Jim Falk, *Global Fission*, Melbourne: Oxford University Press, 1982, p. 112.
33. *Ibid.*, pp. 26-7.
34. *Ibid.*, p. 112.
35. Martin Ince, *Energy Policy*, London: Junction, 1982, p. 93.
36. Tony Benn, 'The Sizewell Syndrome', in *END papers Seven*, Nottingham: Spokesman, 1984.
37. *Evening Chronicle* (Newcastle Upon Tyne), 28 November 1984.
38. Martin Ince, *op. cit.*, p. 75.
39. *Financial Times*, 20 April 1983.
40. Martin Ince, *op. cit.*, p. 63.
41. *Ibid.*, p. 155.
42. *Sunday Times*, 6 September 1981.
43. Michael Tanzer, *op. cit.*, p. 34.
44. Norman Moss, *The Politics of Uranium*, London: André Deutsch, 1981, p. 107.
45. *Ibid.*, pp. 109-12.
46. *Financial Times*, 4 January 1985.
47. *Guardian*, 15 April 1981.
48. Norman Moss, *op. cit.*, p. 133.
49. *Observer*, 16 March 1980.
50. A.D. Owen, 'The World Uranium Industry', *Raw Materials Report*, Vol. 2, No. 4, 1983, p. 13.
51. *Ibid.*, p. 11.
52. Walter C. Patterson, *op. cit.*, p. 81.
53. *Financial Times*, 8 January 1985.
54. *Financial Times*, 25 August 1983.
55. Norman Moss, *op. cit.*, p. 21.
56. See e.g. Barbara Rogers and Zdenek Cervenka, *The Nuclear Axis*, London: Julian Friedmann, 1978.
57. Alan McDonald, 'Exploring the Limits', in Robin Clarke (ed.), *More Than Enough?*, Paris: UNESCO, 1982, p. 26.
58. *Financial Times*, 25 August 1983.
59. N. Passant, *Sizewell Inquiry Documents*, Day 33.
60. Greenpeace, *The Windscale File*, London: Greenpeace, 1982, p. 4.
61. *Financial Times*, 26 November 1984.
62. Colin Sweet, *The Price of Nuclear Power*, London: Heinmann, 1983, pp. 36-7.
63. *Financial Times*, 8 February 1984.
64. Jim Falk, *op. cit.*, pp. 75-9.

65. UKAEA, *The Management of Radioactive Wastes*, London: UKAEA, 1983.
66. *Financial Times*, 3 February 1983.
67. *Financial Times*, 12 November 1982.
68. *Financial Times*, 7 July 1982.
69. *Financial Times*, 9 September 1982; 15 March 1984.

3. Britain's energy resources

1. Central Statistical Office, *Annual Abstract of Statistics*, No. 121, London: HMSO, 1985, Table 8.3.
2. NCB, *Annual Report*, London: NCB, 1982/3, pp. 20-21.
3. HMSO, *Digest of United Kingdom Energy Statistics 1983*, London: HMSO, 1983, Fig. 1.
4. *Ibid.*, Fig. 2.
5. *Ibid.*
6. Department of Energy, *Proof of Evidence for the Sizewell 'B' Public Inquiry*, London: Department of Energy, 1982, Table c.
7. CSO, *Annual Abstract of Statistics*, Table 8.3.
8. *Ibid.*
9. Andrew Glyn, *The Economic Case Against Pit Closures*, Sheffield: NUM, 1985.
10. Nigel Mortimer, *UK Energy Options*, Sunderland (unpublished), 1985.
11. *Financial Times*, 9 May 1984.
12. Department of Energy, *op. cit.*
13. *Financial Times*, 9 May 1984.
14. HMSO, *Digest of UK Energy Statistics 1983*, London: HMSO, 1983.
15. *Financial Times*, 14 January 1985.
16. Department of Energy, *Investment in Energy Supply and Energy Use*, London (unpublished), 1982.
17. *Ibid.*
18. Gerald Leach and others, *A Low Energy Strategy for the UK*, London: IIED, 1979.
19. Network for Alternative Technology and Technology Assessment (NATTA), *Newsletter 27*.
20. NATTA, *Alternative Technology, The Answer to the Energy Crisis?*, Milton Keynes: NATTA, 1981.
21. UK-ISES, *Solar Energy: a UK Assessment*, London: UK-ISES, 1976.

22. NATTA, *Newsletter 25*.
23. Michael Flood, *Solar Prospects*, London: Wildwood House, 1983, p. 97.
24. NATTA, *Alternative Technology, The Answer to the Energy Crisis?*.
25. Michael Flood, *Solar Prospects*, p. 86.
26. *Ibid.*, p. 133.
27. NATTA, *Newsletter 27*.
28. NATTA, *Alternative Technology, The Answer to the Energy Crisis?*.
29. Michael Flood, *op. cit.*, pp. 126-7.
30. *Ibid.*, pp. 114, 118.
31. NATTA, *Newsletter 24*.
32. Michael Flood, *op. cit.*, p. 27.
33. *Ibid.*, pp. 26-7.
34. Alan Roberts, *The Self-Managing Environment*, London: Allison & Busby, 1979, p. 37.
35. All figures calculated from *The Electricity Supply Handbook*, London: Electrical Times, 1984.
36. Department of Energy, *Proof of Evidence for the Sizewell 'B' Public Inquiry*.
37. *Ibid.*

4. The labour movement's record

1. Alex Callinicos, *International Socialism*, 17, Autumn 1982, London, p. 26.
2. John Fernie, *A Geography of Energy in the United Kingdom*, London: Longman, 1980, p. 8.
3. Department of Energy, *Energy Research and Development in the United Kingdom, Energy Paper No. 11*, London: HMSO, 1976.
4. Department of Energy, *Energy Policy Review, Energy Paper No. 22*, London: HMSO, 1977.
5. National Coal Board, *Plan For Coal*, NCB, 1974.
6. *Socialist Review*, April 1984, p. 14.
7. John Fernie, *A Geography of Energy in the United Kingdom*, p. 59.
8. *Ibid.*
9. E.g. Tony Benn, 'The Sizewell Syndrome', in *ENDpapers Seven*, Nottingham: Spokesman, 1984.
10. Alun Roberts, *The Rossing File*, London: Namibia Support Committee (CANUC), 1980.

11. *Guardian*, 21 November 1983.
12. Royal Commission on Environmental Pollution, Sixth Report, *Nuclear Power and the Environment*, (Flowers Report), London: HMSO, 1976.
13. Select Committee on Science and Technology, Third Report, *The Development of Alternative Sources of Energy*, London: HMSO, 1977, Vol. 1, para. 128.
14. Tony Benn, *Arguments for Socialism*, Harmondsworth: Penguin, 1979, p. 90.
15. John Fernie, *Geography of Energy*, p. 144.
16. *Ibid.*, p. 145.
17. TUC, *TUC Review of Energy Policy*, London: TUC, 1981, p. 30.
18. *Undercurrents*, No. 26, Feb/March 1978, p. 5.
19. *Ibid.*
20. TUC, *op. cit.*, p. 30.
21. John Fernie, *op. cit.*, p. 144.
22. Labour Party, *The New Hope for Britain, Labour's Manifesto 1983*, London: The Labour Party, 1983.
23. *New Ground*, No. 3, Autumn 1984, p. 3.
24. TUC, *op. cit.*, p. 17.
25. Dave Elliot *et al.*, *The Politics of Nuclear Power*, London: Pluto, 1978, p. 46.
26. TUC, 1979 Congress Resolution on Energy Policy, in *TUC Review*, p. 126.
27. Martin Ince, *Energy Policy*, London: Junction Books, 1982, pp. 42-4.
28. TUC, *op. cit.*, p. 24.
29. Michael Flood *et al.*, *The Pressurized Water Reactor*, Friends of the Earth Energy Paper No. 4., London: FOE, 1981.
30. TUC, *op. cit.*, p. 77.
31. Gerald Leach *et al.*, *A Low Energy Strategy for the United Kingdom*, Science Reviews Ltd, London, 1979.
32. TUC, *op. cit.*, pp. 33-5.
33. *Ibid.*, p. 84.
34. *Ibid.*, p. 123.
35. *Ibid.*, p. 44.
36. *Guardian*, 9 September 1983.
37. *Ibid.*
38. Dave Elliot, *op. cit.*, p. 45.
39. Martin Ince, *op. cit.*, p. 44.
40. GMWU, *Energy: Planning for the Future*, Esher: GMWU, 1981, p. 14.

5. Tory energy strategy

1. *Financial Times*, 16 November 1984.
2. Martin Spence, 'Nuclear Capital', in *Capital and Class*, No. 16, Spring 1982, p. 10.
3. *Economist*, 25 July 1978.
4. Department of Energy, *Proof of Evidence for the Sizewell 'B' Public Inquiry*, London: Department of Energy, 1982, Tables C and D.
5. HMSO, *Digest of US Energy Statistics 1983*, London HMSO, 1983, Table 56.
6. Michael Flood, *Solar Prospects*, London: Wildwood House, 1983, p. 181.
7. I. Rutledge and P. Wright, *Coal Worldwide: The International Context of the Miners' Strike*, University of Sheffield, 1985.
8. Speech given by Philip Jones, Chairman of the Electricity Council, at Conference on 'The Future of the Electricity Supply Industry', Polytechnic of the South Bank, 25 June 1985.
9. *Financial Times*, 22 March 1983.
10. *Financial Times*, 21 February 1983.
11. *Financial Times*, 9 March 1984.
12. *Financial Times*, 12 October 1983.
13. *Financial Times*, 18 October 1983.
14. Financial Times, 18 January 1984; *Observer*, 16 September 1984.
15. *Ibid*.
16. *Labour Research*, Vol. 70, No. 9, September 1981.
17. HMSO, *Digest of UK Energy Statistics 1983*, Table 24; *Labour Research*, Vol. 70, No. 9, September 1981.
18. *Labour Research*, Vol. 73, No. 9, September 1984.
19. *Financial Times*, 10 July 1984.
20. *Financial Times*, 28 January 1984.
21. See e.g. Ralph Milliband, *The State in Capitalist Society*, London: Quartet, 1973.
22. *Financial Times*, 25 July 1984.
23. *Financial Times*, 1 November 1984.
24. *Financial Times*, 25 July 1984.
25. *Tribune*, 4 February 1983.
26. *Financial Times*, 10 July 1984.
27. Department of Energy, *op. cit.*, p. A3.
28. *Financial Times*, 1 October 1984.
29. *Ibid*.
30. *Financial Times*, 10 January 1984.

6. Alternative energy forecasts and Green politics in the UK

1. R. Todd and C. Alty (eds.), *An Alternative Energy Strategy for the UK*, Powys, Wales: NCAT, 1978.
2. G. Leach *et al.*, *A Low Energy Strategy for the UK*, London: IIED Science Reviews Ltd, 1979.
3. D. Elliot, *Energy Options and Employment*, London: CAITS, 1978.
4. D. Olivier, Hugh Miall *et al.*, *Energy Efficient Futures: Opening the Solar Option*, London: Earth Resources Research, 1983.
5. G. Leach, *op. cit.*, p. 10.
6. Department of Energy, R. Todd and C. Alty, *op. cit.*, p. 30.
7. *Energy Paper 11*, London: Department of Energy, 1976.
8. Department of Energy, *Energy Policy Review*, London: Department of Energy, 1977.
9. Department of Energy, *Energy Commission Paper 1*, London: Department of Energy, 1977.
10. Department of Energy, *Energy Paper 39*, London: Department of Energy, 1979.
11. C.H. Davies, *CEGB P5 – On: Scenarios and Electricity Demand*, CEGB Evidence to Sizewell 'B' Public Inquiry, 1982.
12. D. Olivier, Hugh Miall *et al.*, *op. cit.*, p. xv.
13. Department of Energy, *Proof of Evidence for the Sizewell 'B' Public Inquiry*, 1982, Appendix 2.
14. R. Todd and C. Alty, *op. cit.*, pp. 4-5.
15. *Ibid.*, p. 27.
16. *Ibid.*, p. 25.
17. *Ibid.*, p. 31.
18. D. Elliot, *op. cit.*, p. 55a.
19. *Ibid.*, p. 4.
20. *Ibid.*, p. 111.
21. *Ibid.*, p. 120.
22. *Ibid.*, pp. 122-3.
23. D. Leach, *op. cit.*, p. 9.
24. *Ibid.*, p. 18.
25. D. Olivier, Hugh Miall *et al.*, *op. cit.*, p. xiii.
26. *Ibid.*
27. *Ibid.*
28. *Ibid.*, p. 194.
29. *Ibid.*, p. 51.
30. *Ibid.*, p. xv.

31. D. Leach, *op. cit.*, p. 9.
32. R. Todd and C. Alty, *op. cit.*, p. 25.
33. D. Olivier, Hugh Miall *et al.*, *op. cit.*, pp. 194-6.
34. *Ibid.*
35. Ecology Party, *Politics for Life, 1983 Election Manifesto*, London: Ecology Party, 1983, p. 4.
36. *Ibid.*, p. 34.
37. J. Porritt, *Seeing Green*, Oxford: Blackwell, 1984, p. 226.
38. F. Capra, *The Turning Point: Science, Society and the Rising Culture*, London: Wildwood House, 1982.
39. *Ibid.*, p. 17.
40. *Ibid.*, p. 15.
41. SERA, *New Ground*, London, quarterly.

7. Energy and society

1. Nancy Makepeace Tanner, *On Becoming Human*, Cambridge: Cambridge University Press, 1981, Chapter 7.
2. Karl Marx, *Capital*, Vol. 1, (1867), London: Lawrence & Wishart, 1954, p. 173.
3. Marshall Sahlins, *Stone Age Economics*, London: Tavistock, 1974, p. 43.
4. J.D. Bernal, *Science in History*, Vol. 1, Harmondsworth: Penguin, 1969, pp. 99-100; Rudolf Bahro, *The Alternative in Eastern Europe*, London: New Left Books, 1978, p. 69.
5. *The Ecologist*, Vol. 12, No. 1, 1982.
   16. Edward Hyams, *The Changing Face of Britain*, St Albans: Paladin, 1977, pp. 56-8.
7. Jean Gimpel, *The Medieval Machine*, London: Futura, 1979, p. 21; J.D. Bernal, *Science in History*, Vol. 1, . 314.
8. J.D. Bernal, *op. cit.*, p. 315.
9. J.D. Bernal, *op. cit.*; Jean Gimpel, *op. cit.*, p. 37.
10. Carlo M. Cipolla, *Before the Industrial Revolution*, 2nd edition, London: Methuen, 1981, p. 161.
11. Samuel Lilley, 'Technological Progress and the Industrial Revolution 1700-1914', in Carlo M. Cipolla (ed.), *The Fontana Economic History of Europe: The Industrial Revolution*, London: Fontana, 1973, pp. 190-205.
12. Karl Marx, *Capital*, Vol. 1, pp. 669 and 702.
13. *Ibid.*, p. 352.
14. Karl Marx, *Grundrisse*, Harmondsworth: Penguin, 1973, p. 414.

15. Karl Marx, *Capital*, Vol. 3, Chicago: Charles H. Kerr, 1909, p. 249; Karl Marx, *Capital*, Vol. 1, Chapter XXV; Karl Marx, 'Wage Labour and Capital', (1849), in *Marx/Engels Selected Works in One Volume*, London: Lawrence & Wishart, 1968, p. 81.

16. Renfrew Christie, 'Why Does Capital Need Energy?', in Petter Nore and Terisa Turner (eds.), *Oil and Class Struggle*, London: Zed Press, 1980.

17. Gerald Foley, *The Energy Question*, Harmondsworth: Penguin, 1981, p. 67.

18. Daniel Yergin, 'Crisis and Ajustment: An Overview', in Daniel Yergin and Martin Hillenbrand (eds.), *Global Insecurity*, Harmondsworth: Penguin, 1983, p. 22.

19. Malcolm Slesser, *Energy in the Economy*, London: Macmillan, 1978, p. 18.

20. Michael Flood, *Solar Prospects*, London: Wildwood House, 1983, p. 27.

21. Gerald Foley, *op. cit.*, p. 96.

22. *Ibid.*, p. 67.

23. *Ibid.*, p. 221.

24. Department of Energy, *Proof of Evidence for the Sizewell 'B' Public Inquiry*, Department of Energy, 1982, Tables C and D.

25. *Financial Times*, 23 July 1984.

26. V.I. Lenin, 'Our Foreign and Domestic Position and the Tasks of the Party', (1920), in V.I. Lenin, *On the Development of Heavy Industry and Electrification*, Moscow: Progress, 1972, p. 78.

27. Alec Nove, *An Economic History of the USSR*, Harmondsworth: Penguin, 1982.

28. Alec Nove, *op. cit.*, p. 189.

29. Karl Marx, 'Critique of the Gotha Programme', (1891), in *Marx/Engels Selected Works*.

30. Mike Cooley, *Architect or Bee?*, Slough: Langley Technical Services, 1979.

31. NATTA, *Stealing the Sun*, Milton Keynes: NATTA, 1982.

32. Richard J. Barnet, *The Lean Years*, London: Sphere, 1981, pp. 30-32.

8. Forces for Change

1. Dave Elliot, 'The Future of Coal', in *New Ground*, No. 3, Autumn 1984, Journal of SERA, p. 11.

2. Lucas Aerospace Combine Shop Stewards Committee, *Lucas: An*

Alternative Plan, Nottingham: Institute for Workers Control, IWC Pamphlet No. 55, undated.

3. Martin Spence, 'Nuclear Capital', in *Capital and Class*, No. 16, Spring 1982, London: CSE, p. 9.

4. 'Jobs from Warmth' – leaflet published by TUSIU, Newcastle, 1981.

5. Bill Sheldrick, *Energy Saving and Local Authorities*, London: Association for the Conservation of Energy, 1984.

6. Newcastle Upon Tyne, *Energy in Newcastle*, Newcastle: City of Newcastle Upon Tyne, 1984, p. 10.

7. See for example the evidence of Ipswich Friends of the Earth to the Sizewell 'B' Inquiry.

8. *Guardian*, 14 December 1984.

9. 'Uranium Campaigning', paper produced by PARTIZANS for Southeast Anti-Nuclear Network meeting 1983, unpublished.

10. GLC, *The London Industrial Strategy*, London: GLC, 1985, pp. 40-62; GLC, *The People's Plan for the Royal Docks*, London: Newham Docklands Forum and the GLC Popular Planning Unit, 1983.

9. A socialist energy strategy

1. See, for example, A. Glyn, *The Economic Case Against Pit Closures*, Sheffield: NUM, 1984. This analyses the policy of pit closures by looking at its costs to the country as a whole, rather than simply at the internal accounting procedures of the NCB. Even here, Glyn looks only at immediate financial costs. A full social audit would take into account knock-on effects on other industries and services, lost rate revenue to local authorities, extra costs to the NHS and social services arising out of increased stress and tension in the community, and so on.

2. Alec Nove, *The Economics of Feasible Socialism*, London: George Allen & Unwin, 1983.

3. Malcolm Slesser, *Energy in the Economy*, London: Macmillan, 1978.

4. Gerald Leach *et al.*, *A Low Energy Strategy for the UK*, London: Science Reviews, 1979, Chapter 3.

5. Socialist Environment and Resources Association, *An Alternative Industrial Strategy*, London: SERA, 1981.

6. Stuart Holland, *The Socialist Challenge*, London: Quartet, 1975, Chapter 7.

7. Stuart Holland (ed.), *Out of Crisis*, Nottingham: Spokesman, 1983.

8. Dave Feikart, talk at conference on coalfield communities, Northern College, Barnsley, March 1985.

9. National Coal Board, *Report and Accounts 1982/3*, London: NCB, 1983.

10. Michael Flood, *Solar Prospects*, London: Wildwood House, 1983, p. 29.

11. Amory B. Lovins, *Soft Energy Paths*, Harmondsworth: Penguin, 1978, p. 39.

12. Martin Ince, *Energy Policy*, London: Junction, 1982, p. 155.

Index